# Find the **right** care home

## a step-by-step companion

**Written by Rosemary Hurtley
and Julia Burton Jones**
Foreword by Richard Briers
Illustrations by David Langdon

Published in 2008 by Age Concern Books
1268 London Road
London SW16 4ER
United Kingdom

ISBN: 978 0 86242 428 2

Edited by: Eve Menezes Cunningham
Designed by: David Shaw
Cover photograph: © Peter Adams / Getty Images
Printed and bound in Great Britain by: Latimer Trend & Co Ltd

**Our thanks also go to all the reviewers and contributors:**

Colin Hutchens from the Relatives & Residents Association, Annie Stevenson from My Home Life, Elaine Cobb from The Salvation Army, Cynthia Heymanson, Sarah Selous, Jackqui Franklin, Carol Dilley, Solicitors for the Elderly, Philip Spears from the NCFA. Also to: The Brendoncare Foundation, Paul Bedwell, Nigel Parsons, the Relatives & Residents Association Helpline, Michele Woodger and Surrey Heights Relatives Group, Care Management Matters, Elderly Accommodation Council, Solicitors for the Elderly, English Community Care Association (ECCA).

The publisher would also like to thank David Langdon for kindly contributing the illustrations for this book.

"This book is an excellent, comprehensive guide to a complex and sensitive issue. It will be both companion and compendium to all who have to embark on the journey to find a home including people with dementia and their families."
**The Alzheimer's Society**

"Many older people have to make the decision whether or not to move into a care home at a time in their lives when they are ill or under great stress. *Find the Right Care Home* is a welcome new book to ensure that older people, their relatives and carers can access information and advice so the choice of care home is one suitable to meet all their or their relative's assessed needs."
**Counsel and Care**

"*Find the Right Care Home* is a thoughtful and detailed account of how to make the right decisions and choices when the time comes for a loved one to move into care. Every care home resident is an individual with a unique life history expressed in values, interests and preferences. Care homes need to acknowledge and respond to this and relatives need to know how to identify the homes that do so successfully. The book while targeted at families should also serve as a resource to care home providers and help them tailor their services to meet the needs of their residents in all their variety."
**Relatives & Residents Association**

"Not only a tool to navigate the difficult and confusing journey of finding good quality care but also of immense help in handling the feelings and anxieties that arise. This will be welcomed by many people."
**The Salvation Army**

"Finding a care home is an affair of the heart, as well as of the head. This book understands that and speaks sensibly and sensitively on both counts. Reading this book feels like having the best friend possible alongside you to 'talk it all through' with. Critically and with enormous relief, this friend is not pushy and doesn't at any stage judge or make decisions for you. I wish I had read it sooner!"
**Sarah Sealous, who looked at 63 care homes before finding the right one.**

# Author biographies

**Rosemary Hurtley** is an independent consultant occupational therapist, Care Home Adviser and trainer specialising in developing services for older people in care homes. She is co-founder of the Resident Centered Care Home Standard™ (RCC Home Standard) and a founder trustee of the National Association of Providers of Activities (NAPA).

**Julia Burton Jones** has spent twenty years working (mainly in the voluntary sector) to raise awareness of the needs of family carers and older people. She has a first degree in social administration and sociology, and a Masters in adult and continuing education. She has had development and training roles within several national charities, most recently the Relatives & Residents Association and **_for dementia_**. She is an independent adviser to Care UK on service user involvement and an approved trainer with several organisations, including the Alzheimer's Society.

# Contents

# Acknowledgements

**Rosemary would like to thank:**

My mother Edith.

My husband Charles and children Sarah-Louise and Richard for their generous support, encouragement and badgering.

For inspirational 'sparkling' personal and professional friends for their unique insights and understanding about the essence of compassion and dignity: Sarah Selous, Jackie Pearce, Pat Duff, Julia Pitkin, Annie Stevenson, Amanda Waring, Colin Hutchens and Bob Laventure.

Colleagues in the Relatives & Residents Association.

Friends and colleagues including the 'My Home Life' team.

To all those living and working in the care homes we have worked in.

**Julia would like to thank:**

My husband Simon and children Timothy and Helena, for their support and for believing in me.

Generous and wise friends who have shared their perspectives on the needs of older people and their families and given unfailing encouragement, especially Cynthia Heymanson.

Inspirational care home managers and directors with whom I have had the pleasure of working over recent years. In particular Debbie Christian, Shane Cosgrove, Kathy Harman, Phillip Steyn, Wendy Pike, Lucy Ross, Connie Oppong and Philip Mosley.

The many relatives, residents and staff who have shared with me their insights and experiences, especially the entire care home communities at Laurel Dene and Whitefarm Lodge.

All my friends and colleagues at ***for dementia***, for their passion and commitment to the wellbeing of older people.

**From us both:**

Our wonderfully patient, good-humoured and intelligent commissioning editor, Peter Hooper, and Michael Roche, in the information department at Age Concern, for their invaluable guidance throughout the writing of this book.

# Foreword
# Richard Briers

When looking ahead to our later years, most of us don't plan to spend time in a care home. In fact, it may be something we aim to avoid. We imagine spending our final days in the familiarity and comfort of our own home. While most of us will be able to stay at home, for a sizeable group of older people, the time comes when a care home could be the best place to live. This book is about turning an experience we may fear into a positive choice.

Newspapers and documentaries regularly highlight and uncover abuse of older people. People rarely talk about the countless good experiences of older people in good homes who are able to live fulfilling lives because of the kind support of dedicated staff. Nor the chronic loneliness, insecurity and emotional neglect of some people left alone in their own homes. They might have only the briefest brush with human contact due to overstretched and limited 'care in the community'.

The government policy of encouraging people to seek help in their own home often ignores the small percentage of people for whom a care home is the best option due to their particular needs. To make things even harder, being told only the negative things has a dreadful effect on families who see permanent care as the next step in supporting someone they care about. It only adds to the guilt and anxiety many feel and makes the decision even harder.

This book is born out of personal experience and the realisation that it is not a one size fits all process. It will help you personalise the choices to meet the needs of your family member or friend and make the best decision possible. This book will also help you to put things into perspective and address guilt or anxiety at this complex decision making time. It gives helpful advice on how to support a relative or friend, once they have moved into a home – with your help, they can find a lifestyle that suits them. They can make new friends, have enriching opportunities and be safe and well cared for by skilled and committed staff. The staff's role is to support and enable them to enjoy a good quality of life, recognising the effects of living in a community setting.

Your unique contribution to the life of the person you care for will remain as crucial as ever – your relationship with them is irreplaceable. Hopefully you will find a new network of relationships within the care home too. You will have support as you continue to do your best for your relative. In partnership with the care home staff, you can help make sure their new life is truly 'the good life'.

# Introduction

Finding yourself in an unknown territory can be very stressful and, for most people, finding a care home is a completely new experience. However, some fast track learning will equip and guide you into this arena. This book will take you through a maze of uncertainties, acting as your companion and helping you to avoid pitfalls at each step of the way. We hope it will help you and your relative through a major life change. You will learn how to make the best decisions for your unique situation as you confront unfamiliar roles and emotions.

There are approximately 410,000 older people living in care homes and with an ageing population the numbers are expected to grow. However, people generally don't expect ever to need care. They are often unprepared and unsure of what is available to choose from – let alone how to go about this, often at a time when they are at an emotional and physical disadvantage. They need more than lists of names and addresses to equip them.

The current care system is complex and confusing and we hope that we can tackle the following concerns:

- whether a care home is the right option
- what care is available
- who pays for it
- what choices are available
- how the system works
- moving home and its effects
- practical and financial help available.

The route to finding the right care home is not clear. It can be lonely, confusing and beset with the risk of getting it wrong. There are several choices out there, but which one should *you* choose? The basis of that decision making and its impact on everyone's quality of life requires some specific knowledge and clear guidelines to set you on your way. Unexpectedly propelled into this situation on behalf of another, you may have no former knowledge or understanding.

## Is it the right solution?

The decision to move to a care home is often the right solution for some facing a complex set of circumstances and needs. It is a matching process, like finding the right school for a child. What suits one person may not necessarily be right for another.

Each home has its own personality, culture and ambience when you walk through the door. Sometimes the right choice is straightforward, but for others it takes much longer to find one.

The reasons leading up to this decision are varied and can include physical, psychological, social or mental health factors. One thing is certain: it is always about making the best out of a difficult situation. Some people will be juggling a lot in their lives and feel caught in the middle of the demands of both generations above and below. They are often referred to as the 'sandwich generation'. Life's responsibilities still continue to make their demands and when the unexpected happens, the strain becomes untenable. You are not alone. Rosemary found herself in this very situation.

### Different needs

You may be a carer, struggling to manage to keep your relative at home. You might be trying to delay the inevitable because of the stress of change or fear of the unknown.

You may be feeling anxious or exhausted from providing 24 hour care without a break. Every situation and the relationships involved is unique and the 'trigger' point will be different for each.

One of your parents may have been managing at home with a range of support systems now insufficient for their changing needs. You realise that a decision must be made quickly to prevent the situation breaking down completely.

Other scenarios may involve a relative having a sudden illness, a fall, or rapid deterioration after a spell in hospital so returning home may not be a viable option.

Some people actively choose to go into a home, but this is rare. However, many can be pleasantly surprised by their experience and wonder why they did not think about it earlier. Others find themselves in more challenging circumstances when the right home nearby cannot be found.

The press is often beset with horror stories. Although some poor homes do still exist, there are many good and some excellent care homes to be found. Many of these have to cope with limited resources to meet the increasingly complex needs within care homes around the country. A 'good' home will be a place with proper management and leadership, the right level of investment and understanding of what consumers want and a staff able to deliver this. A care home can be a positive option.

You may also be dealing with various related tasks on behalf of your relative. Organising finances, coping with bereavement, and all the additional jobs to do if their own home is left unoccupied or needing to be sold, not to mention family politics all take time and energy.

## A problem shared

Many people have experienced the extremes of the emotional 'roller coaster' ranging from panic to utter bewilderment. You may fear making the wrong decision. There could be disappointment and frustration when things don't go as smoothly as one would like. Feeling confused and angry and experiencing a sense of powerlessness is common to many who feel hampered by guilt in taking the first step.

# A personal message

Both authors of this book are familiar with the dilemma of choosing a care home, particularly Rosemary, who had to find four care homes between both her parents. Her father had a stroke and her mother was showing signs of late onset dementia. It took three care homes to eventually settle her mother and her dog comfortably. Although there is plenty of information available from a range of sources, there is not much available in one, easily accessible place. Even for a professional, it is not an easy task. That is why we have written this book.

## Personal story from Rosemary

Our story begins with my mother, a former picture restorer and art dealer with late onset dementia. After five years of organising carers to enable her to stay in her own home, the situation broke down as carers found it increasingly difficult to cope with the intensity of the one to one care. My mother was deteriorating and repeated herself constantly. She could also be very unreasonable and demanding at times, with regular mood swings. This was due to the disability. My brother and the carers found it increasingly hard to cope with it emotionally. The carers moved on too quickly to build up meaningful relationships with her.

The time came to diffuse the intensity and find a suitable care home for my mother and her dog. Her dog, Sammy, was her main source of comfort and emotional attachment. After a few weeks, we found a suitable place about 40 minutes away.

The converted manor set in spacious grounds was also suitable for Sammy. The slightly eccentric and spacious home, full of character and quirkiness, was run by an actor and his partner. They had been in business for 15 years. They made a point of developing a friendly relationship with the relatives, making the visiting experience much more enjoyable. The actor regularly ran memorable musical evenings combining poetry reading, parlour monologues and piano recitals.

He aimed to make simple and everyday experiences, such as mealtimes and various other rituals through the day, positive. This was achieved by teaching staff the art of the small friendly hotel's customer care and attention to the 'little things' that matter, delivered with the respectfulness of a bygone era. The dining room seating plan was changed regularly to encourage conversation between residents. This did not always work but it created a sense of anticipation and drama around mealtimes. My mother enjoyed the banter and good humour between staff and residents.

The extensive grounds, where dogs, cats, birds and donkeys shared a relaxed lifestyle was absolute bliss for my mother's dog – just like home. There was a 'nature trail' wheelchair-friendly walk around the grounds, leading through the woodlands. This home was quite unique.

My mother settled at last and even formed a relationship with a gentleman resident. On reflection she seemed much happier than in her latter days at home alone with a carer. Tragically, the home was sold and closed after 18 months. Thankfully, a year or so later, after another two homes (one did not cope well with the dog) my mother finally settled again. She is now the oldest resident in a very different type of home which is nearer my brother and I. Seeing us regularly is an emotional highlight for her and us.

## Other options

A care home is normally considered after exhausting all other options depending on whether the need is long term or short term care. Both of these may require full assessment. Everyone is entitled to a social services assessment whatever their financial situation although it is an option that 'self-funders' are either unaware of or choose not to pursue.

The other care options include:

- additional support from an agency to enable someone to stay in their home with 'that little bit of extra help' or a greater care package where that is necessary, up to 24 hour care
- short stay respite care in a local care home to provide a break for a carer
- a period of short term rehabilitation (intermediate care) for an older person to maintain independence for longer and assist the carer
- intermediate care, which is available in some areas. A minority of care homes provide this service although some have additional therapy services
- your family member moving nearby or to live with you will enable you to regularly provide or supervise the help they need
- moving to a sheltered housing scheme with access to additional support (extra care facilities)
- introducing technology to make the environment safer. Sensors with alarms and equipment can help a person remain independent in daily living and personal care. Tasks such as putting on socks, stretching or reaching, and getting in and out of a bath safely can be assessed by a local authority or an independent occupational therapist
- a care village usually comprises one storey units or bungalows and sometimes has access to a short term rehabilitation unit and day care services. There are some imaginative schemes being developed around the country. They are run by charities, private companies and housing organisations.

All these options are explored in this book.

## Making the decision

By objectively exploring all the options above, you and your relative can decide whether a care home is the best choice or compromise in a difficult situation. This doesn't mean things won't change. Knowing what is most important to your relative and considering their personality, previous lifestyle, interests, preferences and capabilities will be your best guide.

It is the individual, their interests and getting the best fit around what matters to them that should to be at the heart of this decision making process. Considering the wider family needs and maintaining continuity of contact with family and friends is often the most important consideration for an older family member and it can cushion the process of this significant life change and transition.

## Positives of a care home – a message of hope

Despite the continued negative images portrayed in the media about some care homes, many provide a positive contribution to the lives of frail people with increasingly complex needs. Some can offer short stay care, and a few offer short term intermediate care (short term rehabilitation or re-enablement), enabling people to stay in their own homes. They can also provide specialist services for people with dementia and other complex needs including palliative care.

'Home' means different things to different people. In a recent study of quality of life in care homes, *My Home Life* (see **Appendix 2**) highlighted the positive aspects of living in a care home community and the things that are most important to an older person when they are living there.

It can be a place where new relationships can be built and a sense of security can be fostered through competent and sensitive care being available on the spot.

A good home can also offer opportunities to try new activities, maintain interests, form new attachments, enjoy better nutrition and provide immediate care when it is required. Many strive to provide a lifestyle where people can retain their individuality and sense of control over the things that matter day-to-day as part of 'person-centred' care. Life can still go on despite the challenges of disability or frailty. Knowing this is an important message for reassuring your relative and everyone involved in the situation.

## Guilt and loss

Once a decision is made and a care home is considered to be the best option, there are often mixed feelings and guilt for many relatives. This can be magnified if you are helping a relative with dementia who cannot understand where they are. A change of environment can be more daunting and stressful for them in itself. Sometimes, despite every effort to avoid it, a whole range of tactics are used to persuade a person to consider entering a care home, such as overelaborating the benefits of the establishment. In some extreme cases, the pressure can lead some relatives to apparent deception and subterfuge to persuade a reluctant relative (although this is not recommended), depending on the circumstances of the move.

A short visit or trial stay is often the best option. You can gauge how your relative is suited to the environment. It is important to involve the older person in each aspect of the process, according to their capabilities. Do not underestimate the intuition and capabilities of a person with dementia.

When a partner or parent moves into a home, a sense of bereavement may not be too far behind, especially for recent carers. Fear of the home not being up to expectation can also precipitate negative feelings. These reactions, which come and go with different levels of intensity, are dealt with later in the book.

We will help you to get the best environment to match your relative's needs in order to manage the transition in the best interests of everyone.

## Looking after yourself

It is important to look after yourself during this stressful time. Give yourself recovery time, exercise and rest to sustain energy and stamina if you are looking after someone or embarking on this role. It is very important to keep sane by ensuring you have the support of steadying and trusted friends, seeking professional support and guidance when you need it.

## Overview of this book

Each chapter will take you step-by-step through a sequence of events and things to consider from the beginning, from recognising a need and knowing when the time is right, to understanding the range of alternative solutions and additional information available during the search. We will help you look after yourself and cope with the changes and upheaval of a move in circumstances which may be sudden, unpleasant or challenging for both of you. After your relative has moved into the home, we will help you to learn the ropes of care home living.

This includes being a 'visitor', understanding what is expected, how to get involved, dealing with problems and change, right until the end of your relative's stay, and in some cases beyond. Some relatives develop strong associations and relationships with a care home and others decide to maintain the link or even become a volunteer in the home after a relative has died.

We'll cover the following steps in more detail:

**Step One ● Knowing when the time is right**:
the decision making process, what to think about.

**Step Two ● Going through the options**:
what else is available before you finally decide.

**Step Three ● Making your financial plans**:
what you need to know.

**Step Four ● Start looking**:
what to look for in a care home.

**Step Five ● Preparing for the move**:
practical tips to prepare you and your relative.

**Step Six ● Moving in**:
coping strategies to ease a major life transition.

**Step Seven ● Learning the ropes**:
understanding how things work in a care home.

**Step Eight ● Getting involved**:
helping you to become a partner in the care community.

**Step Nine ● Dealing with problems and change**:
how to manage concerns effectively.

**Step Ten ● End of life**:
helping you through the grieving process.

Most people in care homes are referred to collectively as 'residents'. We will be using this term in the book. The system of inspection is moving from the Commission for Social Care Inspection to the Care Quality Commission (as of April 2009). We shall refer to The Inspectorate as a generic term.

# Step One
# Knowing when the time is right

Having set the scene, we can move on to the first step. Step One identifies some of the stresses and strains involved in deciding if and when the time is right for your relative to move into a care home. It is rarely an easy decision to make. This chapter will guide you through the decision making process to ensure the timing and choice is right for you and your relative's unique circumstances. We will cover both the practical and emotional aspects for everyone involved.

Step Two outlines some of the other options you should also consider before you start looking for a care home and will help steer you towards specialist organisations. By taking you through some of the alternatives and their implications, we hope you will be more informed and confident about tackling this new challenge.

## Building up to the decision

Frequently, a move into a care home is suggested because of a crisis, possibly one that has meant a stay in hospital, which means decisions often have to be made quickly. However, decisions made in a hurry, without adequate information, can be complicated by strong and sometimes conflicting advice from family and friends. Knowing if and when the time is right for a care home involves first fully understanding what the options are. Once these are fully explored, it can make all the difference to how a person feels when they finally settle into a new environment. So a degree of planning ahead will always be useful.

Of course, this is likely to be a stressful time for all involved. The thought of moving house in itself can be stressful for your relative. Then there is also the additional adjustment to living in a community with unknown strangers, getting to know new people and fitting into new routines – however flexible they claim to be. You may be a carer who has become too ill or exhausted to continue your caring role and this has forced an emergency unplanned admission in to a care home. This allows little time or energy to plan the whole process properly. Handling this when you are facing other challenges can make you feel inadequate in preparing your family member for such a major life change.

For a successful transition from a home or hospital to a care home, information should be made available to help you. Relatives and professional staff should work together and the patient needs to be involved in decisions wherever possible and supported with kind understanding.

## Changes in the relationship

Taking responsibility for a relative in the process of looking for, settling into and adjusting to a care home requires considerable thought and planning. This new role may bring a change of routine, additional expectations and relationships with health and social care professionals who take over some of your responsibilities in the practical tasks of caring. But whatever the change, don't forget that you will maintain a significant caring role all the way through.

In the case of a parent with dementia, you may find the roles and responsibilities have already started to change. Your parent who was formerly capable and in charge of their life may now move in and out of different time zones. Their ability to understand will require more support due to the effects of the disability.

You may now feel as if you have become a 'parent' to your own parents. For a partner, it is similarly a matter of managing a change of roles within the relationship and constantly adapting to the changes imposed by circumstances.

> Last Christmas, Dad's neighbour rang me. She was concerned she had not seen his lights on for a few days. When I turned up, he had collapsed on the kitchen floor with hypothermia. He may have been lying there for three days. After four months in hospital, we were told he had alcohol related dementia. He was sectioned under the Mental Health Act before his move to a suitable residential home. It was a shock as the signs of dementia were not at all on our radar. Dad does not know where he lives and makes up stories as he cannot separate fact from fiction. We struggled to get information. We did not know what questions to ask or what was expected of us. Yet, now he has settled, we all have a better relationship with him than we have had for years.

## Your role as a carer

The business of caring takes many different forms and there are huge variations in the intensity of help required. Support may be practical, domestic, physical or psychological. If you are a distant carer (a term used for those who live outside the immediate locality and are less able to visit frequently) it doesn't mean you care any less or that you're any less important to your relative. That the relationship may be dependent on the telephone, letter or email makes little difference, even if others are doing the practical tasks. This is an increasing trend as people move around as jobs take them further a field. For frail older relatives, even five miles can seem a huge distance away, particularly if they have transport difficulties.

## Different needs and priorities

You may have found yourself taking on more responsibilities on behalf of your relative (such as helping them to pay the bills, sorting out important correspondence, setting up Powers of Attorney with a solicitor or generally helping with decision making). Whatever the nature of your involvement, prioritise your time, keeping a balance in your life. For some carers, especially spouses, it is a priority to keep their loved one out of institutional care for as long as possible. For others, being unburdened from exhausting caring at home, having the freedom to communicate and interact with their loved one without being a hands-on carer, divorced from the awkwardness of dependency may be exactly what is needed. Other alternatives to a care home are outlined in **Step Two** to help you and your relative decide on the best option.

## Involving people in the decision

Your relative should always be involved in the decision making process even if they may be too frail, mentally and physically, to make decisions on their own without support. This may require you to become their representative or family advocate. You will need to put yourself into the shoes of your parent or close relative and think hard about the things that are important to them. Allow their personality, preferences and previous lifestyle to inform the decisions regarding aspects of their care.

The aim is to help your family member decide as much as they are able to in their best interests and retain as much control over their lives as possible. A person with dementia is still capable of making choices but these need to be presented carefully in different ways or at different times. If they feel insecure or frightened it is not surprising that they react angrily, refuse to co-operate or even deny there is any problem at all. They may fear abandonment or rejection. These emotions need to be acknowledged and understood.

Alternatively, your relative may choose to go into a home to relieve the burden on the family. Concerned about the effect of caring or growing dependency on the quality of their close relationships, they may have decided domiciliary care at home is not for them. Many people feel lonely, helpless or insecure at home. Making the decision to find a care home for your relative or partner is difficult but it can be eased by involving them from an early stage and discussing all of the options available. These are discussed in detail in **Step Two**.

## Getting expert advice

Always remember that expert advice is available and should be taken. For example, if you are prompted to consider a care home for your relative through a sudden change in their behaviour, it is important to investigate possible reasons for sudden changes with a GP. It may be an incident reported by a neighbour or social worker, general confusion or an inability to cope. Whatever the reason, get all the facts straight before decisions are made and have a proper medical assessment by the GP. The problem may be due to something treatable such as an underactive thyroid, adverse side effects of a medicine, an infection, a vitamin deficiency or anaemia. Even a simple build up of wax in the ears can have debilitating effects. Conditions affecting the nervous system may include a stroke, Parkinson's or dementia. Treatments and a period of rehabilitation can improve function. Heart conditions and breathing difficulties can also make independent living difficult and hazardous. Osteoporosis, the bone wasting disease, can lead to increased unsteadiness, falls and fractures.

## Managing the situation

In managing any situation and making the right choice, having the right information is essential. Your relative might be particularly vulnerable and frail, coping with complex or chronic health conditions supported by medications and treatments. For others, there are benefits of timely admission to a care home, where a sense of security and a good quality of life is still possible. They can enjoy new possibilities and relationships as well as get involved in activities. Where there are higher dependency or specialist needs, it is important to ensure that the home can provide the right level of professional support to maintain quality of life (see **Step Four**).

## Life change and loss

Whether moving to a care home is a positive or negative experience depends on the circumstances, availability of the right help and the individual's attitude. Important considerations are:

- the level of physical, mental or material loss
- whether or not a person is depressed
- being relieved of responsibilities
- fearing the unknown or financial loss.

Your relative will face a major life change at a vulnerable stage in life. This is particularly challenging when, as in most cases, there has been no previous thought or preparation. This can result from an unexpected illness or deterioration in circumstances. The way the loss of a former home affects them will depend on the time lived there and emotional investment involved.

'Home' means different things to different people. How many associations, relationships and emotional ties are invested in it? Maintaining independence is more about a state of mind than a physical or geographical matter. Moving to a care home is part of a significant life transition.

It should not be seen as a failure but as relocating to meet changing needs. Ways of easing this transition (moving and settling in) to help your relative adapt to a new way of life will be discussed later.

Moving into a care home can also raise practical concerns. A spell in hospital often has a disabling effect on anyone who stays there for any length of time and it is easy to lose confidence. Loss of roles, identity, routines or familiar surroundings can cause anxiety as well as financial worries, loss of a partner or a loved pet, or loss of independence and control over one's life. Concerns about being a burden on children or being able to manage or maintain property to their own high standards can add to the burden. Coping with the unexpected expense of care at home or the fear of 'the unknown' can also worry many people. So can finances not being spent as they originally intended.

## A change for the better

Although such a decision is always going to be a big step, a number of older people view it as a positive move. Some people don't want the ongoing responsibility of managing a house, garden and all that it entails. Nor do they wish to be a burden on their family. Discuss options with them openly to find out their long term priorities concerning the proximity of family, or retaining independence in a smaller more manageable property.

Some older people fear being alone or managing finances, particularly if this role was managed by a partner. Others worry about being unable to cope with low energy levels and the effects of frailty or poor mobility. Fear of crime can be more disabling than the likelihood of it happening and it can impose real restrictions on normal daily life for a frail older person. Again, in such situations, a care home could be one positive alternative.

## Deciding when the time is right

One of the most difficult decisions you and your relative will need to make is deciding *when* the time is right to make these choices about moving into a care home. Remember that it affects the carer's situation too.

Often, for carers, the strain can become too much and your relative's best interest would be better served by a move into a care home. No matter how reluctant you may be to admit this, there is no shame in it – many carers feel relieved by this (although they might not all admit it).

The effects of dependency on the carer are varied but there are some common steps which lead up to any decision to intervene:

- physical deterioration – as a carer you may not be able to continue to manage the extent either of the emotional or physical care required

- emotional equilibrium – any aspect of change can affect sleep, eating, energy levels and normal healthy activity or can lead to depression. If you are feeling resentful, angry or short tempered after a difficult period of inadequate support, your relative could be at risk of neglect due to the overwhelming stress

- a professional, such as a GP or a social worker, may advise that this is the time to consider other options, including long term care, as they notice a deteriorating situation more objectively

- there may be a lack of adequate community care available to enable you to continue caring

- being too hard on yourself, refusing help from a wider support network, holding back feelings of shame or guilt can result in stress which affects your own physical or mental health and wellbeing

- lack of insight into a condition or coping with someone who is unrealistic about their capabilities can result ultimately in others being at risk.

Carrying the burden of care for another in a family unit can be stressful. It can leave you at risk of breaking down at times of sudden change or illness. Care in the community provides a range of support to those already caring for relatives but usually only to a certain level. It varies according to the availability in your area. Sometimes it is necessary to compromise and share the care with other family members, buy it in from an agency or look for other options to reduce the direct caring role to preserve healthy relationships.

Remember, your relative is entitled to a free care needs assessment from your local council. In addition, the carer is also entitled to a free assessment of their needs. This takes into account the level of support required, health needs, abilities, the environment, welfare and safety. Other health professions may also be involved (such as the GP, nurse or therapist). If a care home is considered as a suitable option a further 'comprehensive', 'single' assessment will be arranged covering physical, psychological, spiritual and social needs.

Of course, you and your relative need to assess the situation for yourselves too. When deciding when the time is right, there are some important considerations to take on board. Here are some questions you can use as a guide to the decision making process and its timing:

- what has changed in the last six months?
- what could your relative manage to do last year that they cannot do now?
- is your relative realistic about this?
- is your relative 'safe' (for themselves and others)?
- what other options are available? (See **Step Two**)
- how important is it to your relative to have people around them and access to others when needed?

In some situations, families might be able to ask their relative if they could list the things they are having difficulties with, perhaps in a diary. They can then detect changes in coping with the important tasks to enable them to remain in their current situation. This can then be discussed together openly as a family.

## Common reasons for admission into a care home

There are many reasons for admission to a care home. Usually, it will be a combination of factors. Here we look at some of the most common ones.

### Physical

Most people go into homes with several complex conditions at the same time. This results in greater dependence on others for daily care. Contributing factors may include:

- severe arthritis
- poor balance
- poor eyesight
- incontinence with mild dementia.

On the whole, the research in this field shows that most dependency problems, some of which require specialist nursing, are due to poor physical health. A large proportion of people in care homes experience difficulties with continence, strokes, arthritis, visual or hearing impairment, a tendency to fall easily, general frailty or a long term condition such as:

- diabetes
- heart problems
- a neurological condition such as Parkinson's.

Loss of function and disability can also be made worse by pain creating general debilitation, continuous fatigue or exhaustion. Pain is a commonly undetected problem. If untreated, this can have far reaching effects on an individual's general mood, appetite or sleep, not to mention on *doing* every day things and general physical activity. Detecting pain can be particularly difficult for people with dementia who have limited communication.

### Dementia

The most common mental health problem seen in care homes, to varying degrees is dementia. A person with dementia often goes into a care home when they have become unsafe in their own home and may cause harm to others, and where families are worried about the consistency of care offered at home. In the case of dementia, although there are warning signs it is often a specific incident that precipitates action. A family suddenly realises the extent of their relative's cognitive deterioration, especially if they are successful at covering up their difficulties and appear socially 'intact'.

### Mental Health

Depression is also debilitating and sometimes disguises itself as dementia. Depression is treatable, but some experts, even GPs, wrongly assume it is part of normal ageing. Depression can be aggravated by isolation, physical illness, loss of mobility, eyesight or hearing, and, most notably, bereavement.

There are other long term conditions like schizophrenia, or severe depression, often combined with other conditions of ageing that require more specialist 24 hour care.

### Carer stress

As mentioned above, the combined stresses of caring can take their toll on people in different ways. In every situation, there is a breaking point when the carer is unable to sustain the support or becomes ill themselves. This breakdown of care at home can often result in the need to look for an alternative solution. Carers UK (www.carersuk.org) provide help and advice for those who are new to care, people having problems balancing work and care, or coping with bereavement and language barriers.

### General anxiety

Some people decide they just do not want the worry or to continue to battle with everyday life. The constant lack of energy makes them feel tired and anxious. Furthermore, the fear of living in an isolated neighbourhood or the effects of bereavement, crime or the loss of a partner can make people crave more security and companionship. In this case, a care home can be a positive option.

### Unsuitable property

Another reason for considering a care home might be when the accommodation becomes unsuitable. It may be too big, isolated or have poor access. There may be too many awkward stairs or it may be unsuitable for adaptation. Some people worry when gardens fall into disrepair because they cannot cope with them any more and don't have suitable help available.

### Family breakdown

Family breakdown can also precipitate the need for a care home, whether due to divorce or a support system breaking down due to illness, relationship difficulties or carer stress.

Respite care can help. This is where a carer is offered a break or a holiday from caring. The individual is offered a place for a short stay, either by private arrangement or after assessment from social services.

### Rehabilitation

Sometimes called 're-ablement', rehabilitation is a broad term to describe a range of solutions. These may include active therapy to address the barriers that prevent a person continuing to live independently, for example, short term mobilisation or providing help to walk a dog. This can be done in certain care homes, some of which may have an arrangement with a local Primary Care Trust.

### Other reasons

A care home might be required in some cases where there is abuse (financial, neglect, physical, emotional or sexual), loneliness, isolation or even homelessness. Good nutrition, stimulation or companionship can be provided under one roof.

# The pros and cons of care homes

## Advantages of moving into a care home

- Having 24 hour care in one place with a team of people who regularly change shifts reduces the burden of care.

- The continuity of care and security of being able to raise help when needed may relieve anxiety for people. Otherwise, they might become dependent on domiciliary visits which can be erratic and untimely creating insecurity.

- Quality of life may be seen to go down by moving into a care home but a lot of people settle well, adapt and enjoy a new way of living with more security and support.

- No responsibility for running and maintaining a home and all that is entailed. They will no longer need to shop and cook meals, which can be a real struggle for many. Particularly at a time in life when getting the nutrition necessary to stay well physically and mentally is so important.

- The burden of care is reduced. For some spouses and partners, being unburdened from exhausting care in the home can help them to rekindle former aspects of their relationship, without the awkward burden of care giving.

- Having time to try new activities may be a bonus to some people to prevent boredom and loneliness. Previous life may have been determined and constrained by having just enough energy to do the basic chores.

- Companionship opportunities like new friendships can be made. Sharing with others helps to prevent loneliness, isolation and provide an opportunity for new relationships to blossom. Good care homes help residents get to know each other and build a sense of community. People can join in as far as they wish. An inevitable part of living in a community is that there are possibilities for new friendships and attachments to form as well as maintaining long standing ones.

- Provides opportunities for 'inter-dependence' within a caring community.

- More flexibility and choice as to when care is delivered during the day.

- More potential for supervision or training of staff on the job due to easy access of other staff members.

- Better standard of accommodation for those whose home has been poorly decorated or heated, or difficult to maintain and clean.

11

## Disadvantages of moving into a care home

- Independence: Losing the independence of running one's own home is particularly important to some people, especially when it is closely associated with their identity.

- Control: It can mean a loss of freedom and decision making control. Some like to have their own routine or live a more flexible lifestyle, although it must be said that many good homes work hard to provide flexible care to suit individual preferences rather than to suit the organisation. Loss of familiar surroundings can make one feel insecure and dependent.

- Space: Personal space may be limited and having to adjust to life in a community is more challenging for some people than others. Those who like a lot of space and to have their furniture and possessions around them may struggle with living in a more confined space.

- Familiarity of surroundings, roles and routines: this may be lost or be difficult to adapt to.

- Ownership: Others may resent the legal status of being in a care home and see it as less than being a tenant in rented accommodation, living under the terms of the contract agreed between them and the care home. There are concerns about how this contract could be threatened if at some stage the finances ran out and your relative might be made homeless or require 'top up' fees from another source, which might cause an additional burden on the family. A few new models of care homes are starting to address the tenancy conflict more creatively by offering people a choice to buy accommodation for duration of stay and pay separately for care and thus protect their investment (technically this is extra care sheltered housing).

- Change: For people with dementia, or suffering from a deteriorating illness, the insecurity of having to move on to a specialist home and the accompanying resettling required may be very difficult to adapt to. Some people who feel pressured into moving into a home against their will can have problems adapting to the idea and may even feel pressurised or 'dumped' by their relatives.

Adapted from Shoard M, *A Survival Guide to Later Life*, Constable and Robinson with The Daily Telegraph, (2004).

# Family matters

## Sharing responsibilities

A relative moving into a care home affects the whole family. Helping a parent into a care home may be shared between brother(s) and sister(s). Ill will or conflicting family agendas can make discussions emotionally charged. It can be stressful, even in families where relationships are normally good. Most families live apart, and some family members may live abroad. It is helpful to agree how to share the workload between family members. Although normally the person living closest to the parent is expected to do most of the practical work, some tasks can be split between siblings such as managing the finances or doing the caring or research. It is likely that a parent will want to be nearest to the person who will visit most often or whom they agree will take this responsibility. Sometimes gender stereotypes can come into play and cause tension between brothers and sisters. You may find it helpful to break down tasks and share them between you according to your strengths. One person may be better suited to helping with the finances while another is better at the caring role.

## Conflict

It is not unknown for the apparent 'favourite' son or daughter to be given all the praise, when in fact, the person doing all the work feels unappreciated by a parent. It is helpful to have an open agreement between family members beforehand. Divide tasks fairly to preserve the equilibrium of family dynamics.

Depending on the relationship with the parent, it can be difficult to accept the changes in a parent. Sometimes they can play one child off against the other bringing past tensions, jealousies and guilt to the surface. Every family has different relationship dynamics.

## Finances

Matters of inheritance and the financial implications need to be addressed and understood by all parties (see **Step Three**). Some people find it easier to discuss these matters on neutral territory. It is helpful to list the problems with possible solutions and, where there are communication difficulties, invite a trusted family friend or someone objective to take a mediating role. Keeping the lines of communication open between all parties is important. Where there are relationship difficulties, it is helpful to lay down some ground rules to prevent being accused at a later date. Allow everyone to have their say.

## Roles reversed/shared with others

It may be likely at this stage that caring roles are reversing, if they have not already, and some find this more difficult to cope with than others. Try to keep your parent/partner involved where possible, to help them still feel in control and in the 'driving seat'. Where there are communication or cognitive difficulties you probably will need some professional guidance. This person can help to moderate emotions, be objective and act as an advocate for your relative's best interests.

## Preserving relationships between partners

Having a partner move into a care home will have far reaching effects on the relationship and the individual. Some of the emotional aspects may include the following:

- loss of a companionship and former relationship, enforcing role changes
- loss of the future you may have planned together
- loss of a lifestyle once taken for granted
- challenges posed by a new role in an unfamiliar area
- having control over another person's life
- dealing with manipulation and emotional blackmail
- dealing with accusations from your relative, who may feel insecure, fearful of the unknown, or of being separated from their family and familiar home surroundings
- feeling inadequate
- feeling trapped.

Partners and spouses will want to preserve that sense of being a couple and also avoid feeling lonely. Some people resolve this by moving into the home together or by one partner moving closer to the home.

Derek lived with his wife, Lesley, for 57 years. They are a devoted couple and have two children who live locally and visit regularly. Lesley has insulin-controlled diabetes. A stroke left her unable to walk unaided. Derek has to get up in the night to help Lesley to the bathroom. He has recently had problems with his eyesight and blood pressure. He finds it hard to manage his wife even with considerable help from an outside agency and the district nurse. He is concerned he might not be able to meet his wife's needs. His GP suggested a period of respite care for Lesley. This prompted Derek to find a home with a large room where they could stay together but where he would not have to manage the daily responsibility of the care.

## Coping strategies

Some people can accept a situation more easily. Others may deny or suppress the problem to protect their feelings. Coping with an emergency, small changes or general decline can release powerful feelings of loss or anxiety. You may even feel resentful about the restrictions placed on your own life or feel unhappy that things have not turned out as you might have hoped.

Feelings fluctuate. Trying to maintain your integrity and your desire to do the best you can for the person you are caring for often requires some compromise. You are not the only one who feels guilty or sad. Be more forgiving of yourself and realise there is no perfect solution or perfect carer. It is normal to feel angry, frustrated and out of control when things are unclear or people try to take control around you. It is also not uncommon to want to walk away from the situation.

These coping strategies may help:

### Sharing with others

Consider your own needs, especially if you are a primary carer – it will sustain you in the long run. Visiting or talking things through with a supportive friend, trusted professional or relative will help you keep in touch while remaining in contact with the wider world. Seeing the bigger picture can help you to keep things in perspective. Spend time with someone who is understanding and can make you laugh and even see the funny side of life. There are likely to be good days (when you feel more positive and able to cope) and bad days (when you feel resentful about your relative or the situation you find yourself in). This is normal.

### Exercise

Taking exercise (even walking in the countryside or a local park) can help you to assimilate what is happening and think objectively. Physical activity is a proven way to beat depression and raise mood.

### Interests

If you are of a practical disposition, make a cake or do some DIY or something creative, enjoyable and satisfying. Cleaning a car, gardening or doing something completely different can help.

## Expression

Acknowledge how you feel, don't bottle these feelings up or deny them. Sometimes it will be necessary to relieve the tension by doing something physically exerting. If you are creative, draw, paint or write, use relaxation techniques or listen to music. Writing down feelings/options sometimes helps to put things in perspective making the situation more manageable.

## Get professional help

If you are feeling particularly low or anxious, lacking enough sleep, it may be time to see your GP. Feelings of sadness, regret or anxiety are normal but if they are sustained, they may prevent you doing what you need to do during the course of a normal day. Depression can set in and this is harder to deal with once it has taken its grip.

## Attitude

Think positively, take one day at a time and acknowledge the little steps. All this will help you to be more positive and hopeful. Take time to reflect and actively adopt a 'thankful attitude' for the little things. This will help to strengthen you psychologically and emotionally.

## Investigate other sources of support

Help lines which may help you to talk through your situation include:

- the Relatives & Residents Association
- the Alzheimer's Society
- Carers UK
- Counsel and Care

More information on these organisations can be found in **Appendix 2**.

Richard managed to cope with his wife Joan's depression and anxiety for several years. When he found himself becoming unable to sustain the energy to continue, his family were torn over what to do. They concluded that finding a home nearby would prevent the burden affecting his health. Richard had been housebound but now decided to join a walking group twice a week. He met new people including one who had recently become widowed and understood his concerns. The friendship and the fresh air made Richard feel refreshed and better able to cope when he visited Joan.

## Summary

## Step One ● Knowing when the time is right

- Decisions made in a hurry, without considering other options, can lead to unnecessary stress.

- Your role changing does not mean that you care less.

- It is important to involve your relative in the decisions where possible. Act in their best interests (considering personality and preferences).

- There are professionals and charities who can support and guide you.

- Every situation is unique and there are pros and cons you need to weigh up.

- Consider the impact of the move on the wider family.

- Get support and look after yourself, too, at this time.

# Step Two
# Going through the options

When an older person has extra needs, it is easy to jump to the conclusion that a care home is the next step. However, before you decide to look at care homes, think through alternatives that might enable the older person to continue living independently. It is government policy, locally and nationally, to help people stay at home for as long as possible unless the services of a care home are needed. If your relative has their own money to pay for help, it can be harder to access help in going through the alternatives to a care home. This advice often comes through social services for people needing financial help.

Most older people want to stay in their own home so take time to consider all the resources which might make this possible for your relative. It may mean getting more support, adapting their home or looking into other types of housing. When you have exhausted these options, look into the different types of care home described later in the chapter.

# Ways of staying at home

## Getting more help

Your relative may be receiving some help with day-to-day living. Would it be possible to get them some extra support with things they are finding difficult? Some of this help may be set up through social services but you could also make private arrangements:

### Domiciliary care: arranged privately or through social services

Is your relative having problems with the 'activities of daily living'? Things like getting up and dressed in the morning, taking a bath or shower, going to the toilet or getting ready for bed at night? Home carers (trained in manual handling, managing hoists and equipment, first aid and food hygiene) can visit the person. The cost is usually between £6 and £14 an hour and those who live in rural areas may have to cover travel costs. In some areas care agencies are over-stretched, meaning a wait of a few weeks before they can respond to a request, even for those who pay themselves. Carers UK provide information for relatives and service users to help them think of every eventuality: www.carersuk.org offers information about alternatives. The Commission for Social Care Inspection (to be called the Care Quality Commission as of April 2009) has lists of registered agencies at www.csci.org.uk and the United Kingdom Homecare Association at www.ukhca.co.uk has details, too.

Your relative may already have home carers visiting but an extra call a day from the agency might meet new needs. If social services are organising the package of support, they can reassess how much home care is needed. If you are making your own arrangements, you could time the visits to cover the tasks with which the person is struggling. For people who meet social services eligibility criteria, there is a system of direct payments so you can pay your carers directly out of the budget social services give you. Direct payments only cover personal social care services. There are also individual budgets which broaden the scope of what the money can be spent on. Contact your local Age Concern for more information. A lot of older people are understandably anxious about taking on responsibilities for employing paid carers but it may be an option worth considering.

### Sitting services/respite services, to give the carer a break

Your main concern might be your own health and wellbeing, or the health of a relative who is caring (such as your other parent or a sibling). Caring for a long time without a regular break is likely to lead to health problems, especially for an older carer. Many carers, however, are reluctant to give up their full-time caring role. Being encouraged to take 'respite' breaks is an alternative. This could be breaks of several hours at a time or overnight breaks. There are lots of options for getting respite as it has been a main emphasis of the government but availability will vary depending on locality.

Relief carer schemes such as Crossroads (www.crossroads.org.uk) send a care attendant to the person's home regularly to 'take over' from the carer for a few hours. They can have a rest or go out for a few hours, sometimes overnight, though you may have to wait a few weeks before Crossroads can help if demand for their services is high. Social services may also be able to arrange a break of a week or a fortnight several times a year. Usually this would involve the person needing care going into a care home.

Lots of carers feel taking a break will not be in the interests of the person they are looking after. They need encouragement to see how important breaks are in maintaining their own strength so they can continue caring. Social services can carry out a 'carer's assessment' to identify the carer's needs and inform the 'package of support' which is put in place. Under law, carers have the right to have their needs assessed at the same time the person they are looking after is being assessed. The carer can also be assessed in their own right if the person they are caring for refuses to be assessed. It is a statutory duty to inform carers about carers assessments and to offer an assessment. For more information about carers assessments and your rights, contact Carers UK.

Sylvia had a succession of coughs and colds two winters after her husband Ken's stroke. She seemed unable to shake off infections. After a series of visits to her GP for antibiotics, he suggested her immune system was struggling because she was over-tired and stressed. He urged her to look into respite care options. Knowing how reluctant she was to get help, he warned her that if she didn't look after herself her own health would break down. Sylvia could see the sense in what the doctor was saying and decided to make contact with social services.

## More day care support

Day care is another way of giving full-time carers a break. It can also be beneficial for an older person living on their own. There are a range of options, from informal 'lunch-clubs' run by local organisations (you can contact them yourself) to sophisticated services offering care to people with high level needs (for which you would need a social services referral). Day care is normally provided in a day centre, care home or day hospital. Some people attend one day a week, others several days a week. Most operate only on weekdays but some are starting to open weekends. There is usually transport to collect clients and drop them home in the afternoon. They typically spend part of the day doing activities of various kinds and are provided with a good lunch and refreshments. Sometimes other services, such as hairdressing, are available. Day centres cater for differing needs, so, for example, some would be unable to take a person with a diagnosis of dementia. Some cater for particular ethnic groups.

## Sources of friendship to overcome isolation

For some people, particularly those living on their own, loneliness can be a problem. Do some research to find out about your relative's local area. There may be lunch clubs or friendship circles nearby run by community organisations like churches. The local adult education service will have classes, as may U3A (University of the Third Age). Start contacting local charities working with older people. Our Age Concern branches often have a wide variety of activities and may know of other groups. The Alzheimer's Society local branch may have social events. Many now have regular 'Alzheimer's cafes' where people with dementia and their carers can socialise. Older people's organisations may co-ordinate befriending schemes aimed at reaching out to older people. Some areas run intergenerational projects bringing children and young people together with elderly people.

## Help running the home and garden

Perhaps the house and garden are proving too much for your relative. Could you look into sources of paid or voluntary help for gardening, DIY or housework? There may be a local charity which provides this sort of assistance or you could use a private agency. Social services should be able to point you in the right direction. Try ringing your local Council for Voluntary Service (CVS), or your local Age Concern may run a handy person scheme.

### Shopping services and meals delivery

Again, some local charities operate a shopping service for older people. These may be funded by the local authority or you may have to pay a contribution towards the volunteer's expenses. If getting to the shops is a problem, look into sources of free or subsidised transport for older people in the area. There are options for delivered meals, often provided by the WRVS (Women's Royal Voluntary Service) in partnership with social services. Private companies also deliver frozen meals.

## Adapting the house

You may have identified that your relative's house is their main obstacle. They may struggle getting around a home that was neither built nor bought with disability in mind. Negotiating stairs may be hard, getting in and out of the bath may be difficult or furniture and work surfaces might be at the wrong level.

### Occupational therapy assessment of any equipment that might help

Occupational therapists (OTs) are professionals who help people manage disability and maximise their independence. The occupational therapist can assess a person's needs and work out how their environment could be adapted. The occupational therapist would visit your relative's home and observe and assess how they were coping and make recommendations for altering the house and acquiring equipment. They might also suggest different ways of doing things to save energy, as well as practical coping strategies for keeping safe and maintaining quality of life. Social services can arrange for an occupational therapy assessment as part of the process of assessing care needs. If you are assessed as needing any equipment it will be free, as are any minor adaptations (up to the value of £1,000). You should also check whether you are entitled to receive any Disabled Facility Grants. You can also arrange a private occupational therapy assessment (contact the College of Occupational Therapists for a list of private practitioners in your area on 020 7357 6480 or at www.cot.org.uk).

Since April 2008, the way local authorities offer help with equipment is more of a 'retail model'. A growing number of towns have shops where equipment is available to try out with a qualified OT on hand to advise. If you are assessed as needing and equipment by social services or the NHS, you will get a prescription and the equipment will be free (although you can add to it if you want some better equipment).

### Alterations to the property to make it more safe and accessible

Lots of things we do without thinking become very difficult if we have limited mobility or are in a wheelchair. Getting through doors, manoeuvring around corners, going down narrow corridors can all become hard. Domestic bathrooms are rarely designed with limited mobility in mind. An OT can suggest adaptations including grab rails on steps or in bathrooms, ramps, a wet room instead of a shower, or a stair-lift. If the main carer is struggling with moving the person, hoists can be fitted to help them get the person in and out of bed, for instance. Your local home improvement agency, which might be called 'Care and Repair' or 'Staying Put', will be able to offer guidance. If concerns are more about security, a crime prevention officer from your local police force will come out to advise on security fittings. A useful web tool has been designed to help you assess how well the home is suited and offer some solutions. This is called the HOOP (Housing Options for Older People) tool and is on Housing Care's website (www.HousingCare.org).

### Changing the use of rooms (such as moving the bedroom downstairs)

Another way round problems with the home is to think about changing rooms round. Could the bed be moved downstairs so that the person no longer needs to cope with stairs? If there is no downstairs toilet, is there space to add a small bathroom?

## Assistive technology – aimed at independence and/or safety

There is a burgeoning industry in aids and appliances to help people with disabilities. Several websites (listed at the end of the book) bring together information about pieces of equipment – some complex technologies, others simple devices. If walking has become a problem, you may want to look at options for buying a scooter or electric wheelchair (advice from an occupational therapist is helpful when considering these larger pieces of equipment). Zimmer frames come in lots of shapes and sizes. There is equipment to help people with arthritis to do up buttons or put on tights. There are kitchen utensils to make tasks easier. Specialist equipment is available to compensate for sensory loss (such as telephones with large numbers on the pads to make dialling easier or devices which alert deaf people to the doorbell ringing). Technology can also carry out simple tasks automatically, such as turning on lights.

Many towns have shops which sell and display a range of such equipment so that you can try it out before buying. It is important, for instance, to buy a wheelchair that fits the person who will be using it. Other sources of advice on technology might be your local Red Cross and the helpline of the Disabled Living Foundation.

There is a growing range of products designed to support them and keep people with dementia living alone safe. There are even computer systems, known sometimes as 'telecare', which track a person's movements in their home and whether the gas or water has been left on, alerting a relative if anything out of the ordinary happens. There are alarm call systems where the older person wears a pendant which allows them to call for help if, for instance, they have a fall. In the last few years many local authorities have set up display centres where you can look at equipment. And there is also a new website with information about assistive technology for people with dementia called www.atdementia.org.uk. See also www.telecare@csip.org.uk.

## Releasing capital

Many older people are 'asset-rich' but 'cash-poor'. They cannot afford to buy the help they need, but own homes of considerable value. One option for covering the costs of extra help might be to release some of the capital from the home to pay for care. These decisions are of critical importance in planning the future, so it is good to seek independent legal and financial advice before proceeding. Age Concern publish a book called *Equity Release Made Easy* that may prove to be useful if this is an option you are considering.

## Altering housing arrangements

### Live in help

You can arrange for a full-time live-in carer to look after your relative, much as you might organise a nanny or au pair to look after your children. This is unlikely to be a low-cost option but, if you find the right person, it will give you and your relative peace of mind. Most agencies supply a rota of staff who live in, but, occasionally, the same person is allocated on a longer term basis.

Agencies providing care of this kind are regulated by the Care Quality Commission (you can read their reports at www.cqc.org.uk). In some parts of the country, particularly larger cities, there are schemes where an older person in need of a bit of support offers a room in their house rent free in exchange for practical help, though this would not include help with personal care (www.homeshare.org.uk).

## Co-housing options

A well-recognised way of responding to an older person's growing needs is the idea of a 'granny flat' or 'granny annex'. The older person sells their house and their son or daughter has their home adapted so they can live alongside them. They have their own front door and personal space but help is at hand. Another option is for older people who have been living alone, say two widows or widowers, to decide to share a house and support each other.

## Accommodation options on the market

**Adapted housing** is housing suitable for people with different disabilities. The Home Improvement Agency (HIA) specialise in providing advice and support. Contact Foundations at www.foundations.uk.com or telephone 01457 891909.

**Retirement housing and retirement villages** are an increasingly popular option. They include anything from a block of flats to an entire village, built especially to meet older people's needs. Housing can be bought or rented and is purpose-built and low maintenance, usually set within landscaped gardens which are maintained within the service charge. There may be a shop, restaurant, bar, library, games room and community hall. Pets are usually permitted and schemes tend to have easy access to public transport, though some residents still drive. You and your relative would, however, need to consider their future needs should their health deteriorate. Could their needs be met or would they have to move?

**Sheltered/supported housing schemes** offer your relative the independence of living in a self-contained purpose-built flat or bungalow, supervised by a scheme manager who provides support in an emergency. Sheltered housing and retirement housing provides more security and companionship and it is also possible to receive domiciliary help in this environment.

The flat can be purchased or rented and many run events and have communal areas to socialise. Housing Care provides extensive information (www.HousingCare.org).

**Extra care housing** provides a higher level of support, falling somewhere between traditional sheltered housing and residential care. Again, it is housing that can be rented or bought. Designed with the needs of the frailer older person in mind, these offer a range of support on site and are often run by housing associations and local authorities. There are communal facilities, such as a lounge, a hairdresser, domestic support and a dining room where meals are served, and 24 hour emergency support is provided by a warden. The warden can 'signpost' other services available, but does not provide personal care themselves. With extra care, you have much of the support in residential homes, but the benefit of your own front door and the legal rights to occupy the property. This option allows couples to stay together and have control over finances.

**Close care schemes with care available on site** are when sheltered housing is built within the complex of a nursing or residential home. It allows people to stay in the same place. A range of services can be bought in from the adjacent care home. These schemes are gaining popularity around the country and offer a flexible solution, allowing people to move between different levels of care depending on need. This gives continuity, with people feeling they are known individuals, and also helps maximise independence.

**Intermediate care** is a suitable option when your relative has left hospital but requires rehabilitation to help them manage by themselves. The service is usually provided by the NHS and lasts up to six weeks. Social services should advise over choices in your area (this is often provided in their own home).

**Ownership** is a very recent development. These are essentially a form of extra care housing. A person can buy a room or bedsit and then pay for care on top. The costs for care are graduated depending on how much support the person needs. It means that the person can sell the room if they move on. Being a tenant or owner can give an older person a greater feeling of being in control so perhaps this model will be seen increasingly in the future.

# Types of care homes

## Types of care provided/registration categories

Care homes have to be registered to care for certain needs. To gain registration, they must show they have the necessary facilities and staff skills. There is little point viewing a care home that only takes people with dementia if your relative does not have dementia. Find out what age group they are registered to take and what kind of needs they can meet.

Although there are no longer separate registration categories, you will often find homes offering either personal care or nursing care. Homes which give personal care (which used to be called 'residential homes') employ care staff to give support and use district nurses to meet nursing needs. Homes which give nursing care (which used to be called 'nursing homes') also employ their own nurses 24 hours a day. They have higher ratios of care staff to residents. Fees for care homes giving just personal care are normally lower because the staff ratio is less and they don't employ qualified nurses. Nursing care is subsidised by the NHS. Personal care is means tested in England and Wales but in Scotland a payment of £149 is made. For those with substantial physical or mental health needs, a continuing care assessment can be carried out. This may result in the NHS paying for all the care. A care needs assessment will show the kind of care your relative needs. Some homes have units for both types of care. There is more information about assessment and finances in **Step Three**.

## Different ownership (private/voluntary sector/corporate/NHS/local authority)

Until quite recently, many homes providing personal care were owned and run by local authorities. During the 1980s, when funding was provided by the DHSS, many new independent homes were established in addition to local authority homes. Now many of the local authority homes have been transferred to independent organisations. Social services fund and arrange placements. But they tend not to be the ones delivering the care. Having said that, a few homes dotted round the country are still run by local authorities. So if they are not run by social services, who does run them? Most care homes are operated 'for profit' by individuals or large corporates (for example, banks, venture capital) or 'not for profit' charitable organisations. The few remaining homes within the NHS give continuing care of a very specialist nature. NHS-funded places are usually in independent homes.

Companies and charities which own care homes vary in size and scope. Some own just one home, or a handful in a limited geographical area. Others are large organisations with homes all over the UK. A great many homes are in the hands of a single proprietor, who may employ a manager to run the business. Apart from NHS homes, homes have to be registered with the national regulatory body, the Care Quality Commission (CQC), which ensures that the registered person is fit for the job.

## Specialist homes (for occupational groups, faiths, cultures and so on)

Most care homes cater for all sections of society and their residents represent a social mix. A few places, however, are specialist homes for certain groups of people. This might be an ethnic group; for instance there are many homes for Jewish people, particularly in London. Or it might be for people from a particular occupational background, such as homes for retired teachers, actors, service men or women, or for people who have worked in certain trades (like the motor trade, for instance). Some homes have their origins in a religious grouping, like Methodist Homes. It does not always mean you have to share the background or beliefs, but it gives you an idea of the philosophy of the home.

## Special needs met by care homes

### Dementia

The biggest special category of need met by care homes is dementia care (registration initials DE). Places can be registered for dementia in nursing homes and in homes that provide personal care. Having a dementia does not necessarily mean you will be in a care home registered for dementia care. A 2007 study by the Alzheimer's Society, *Home from Home*, found that two-thirds of older people in care homes had dementia. But of these, 40% were not in a specialist dementia care home.

Dementia is an umbrella term, so you will find some residents have Alzheimer's disease, some may have a vascular dementia (stroke-related conditions), some may have lewy-body dementia (linked with Parkinson's disease) and others rarer types of dementia. Residents will be at different stages of dementia, though people tend not to go into a care home until they are in the middle or later stages.

Nursing homes for people with dementia have mental health nurses to support people with more complex needs and challenging behaviours. There tends to be a high demand for specialist dementia care and you may have to wait for a place.

## Sensory disability

If your relative has particular problems with sight or hearing, you will need to make sure the home can meet their needs. Most care homes should be able to accommodate a person with sight or hearing loss, as these are common in later life, but be mindful of the building layout and décor and the extent to which it will help or hinder. Ask about available equipment (such as a loop system to help people with hearing loss navigate public places) and what training staff receive.

## Strokes and neurological conditions

Stroke and neurological disability are common in later life so most homes have experience supporting individuals with these needs. Some homes are particularly well set up to care for people in this situation. Ask if the home has links with local professionals such as occupational therapists, physiotherapists and speech and language therapists. This will enable better outcomes as there will be access to appropriate advice and treatment. Some homes employ their own part-time therapists.

## Mental health needs

Mental health needs have traditionally fallen alongside dementia in the registration category 'EMI' ('elderly mentally infirm'). Some homes do care for people with dementia and people with enduring mental health problems (bipolar disorder, schizophrenia, depression and so on) in the same units. There are more homes now, though, with units specifically for people with dementia or people with mental health problems. At least 40% of all older people in care homes are believed to have depression, though many are undiagnosed and untreated.

## Learning and cognitive disabilities

If your relative has a learning or cognitive disability there are other considerations to take into account. For example, you may be asked to consider where they should be once they have reached the age when they fall into the 'old age' category.

People with Down's syndrome have a high risk of developing Alzheimer's disease at an earlier age than in the general population (36% of people with Down's aged 50–59 have Alzheimer's as do 55% of those aged 60–69). There are few specialist units for older people with learning disabilities and dementia.

## Cultural needs

Some cultural needs are better catered for in later life than others. But it may be that there are no specialist homes for your relative's ethnic group near enough for them to be able to stay in touch with friends and family. How important is it for them to live in an environment which is culturally familiar? Do they need those around them to be speaking their language? Will it be possible to meet cultural needs (such as religious observance and diet) in a general home? With dementia, for example, people who learned English as a second language often revert to their first language as the dementia progresses.

## Continence issues

Another consideration is the extent to which the home is able to accommodate people with continence problems. Do they have the necessary facilities and equipment and access to continence advice? What is the home's approach and are they able to access information on best practice in continence management?

## Some other considerations

### Legal and financial considerations

Care homes providing personal care cost from around £400 per week. Those providing nursing care charge from about £600 per week, depending on the area you live in and the type of home. The next chapter, **Step Three**, will give you more information about the financial aspects of being in a care home. There are complex issues to resolve so it is worth consulting an independent financial advisor or solicitor at this stage. Issues might include your relative wishing to re-write their will, inheritance tax issues, writing a 'living will', looking at equity release schemes, your relative making a Lasting Power of Attorney and dealing with the Court of Protection.

Think about the long-term, maximising income to cover commitments to meeting fees over a number of years. Are there sources of financial support your relative could tap into, such as benevolent funds for people from their line of work?

## Talking through options together

It may not be easy talking with your relative about what they want from a care home, particularly if they have already told you they do not want to go into a home. By discussing their preferences with them they may slowly come round to accepting what is happening. Research has shown that where people are involved in choosing the home, they find it easier to settle and come to terms with the transition. Avoid rushed decisions. Choosing the right care home is a major step and deserves time for reflection and discussion.

> Peter felt too nervous to discuss the possibility that his mum Margaret might, at some stage, need to go into a care home. They had always been close and he hated hiding things from her, but he knew how fearful she was of going into a home. He didn't have the heart to bring up the subject. But after talking with his neighbour and friend, Jenny, Peter realised that delaying the discussion would probably do more harm than good. As Jenny said, talking about going into a home well before it was necessary would perhaps help Margaret work through her anxieties and prepare them both psychologically for what lay ahead.

There may be some conflict in discussions within the wider family, too. Members of the family who are less involved day-to-day may not understand the reality of the situation. They may think it is possible for your relative to stay at home. Consult everyone from the start, rather than presenting them with a decision from which they feel they have been excluded. Who are the most important people to your relative? They may have elderly friends and neighbours who don't have their own transport but who play a significant part in their life. Choosing a care home even in the next town may prevent them from visiting regularly.

> Jack wondered why his sister Julie was giving him the cold shoulder. She had not been in touch, he realised, for a few weeks. He had been so preoccupied trying to find a home for their mum, Josie, he had not noticed the silence at first. When he rang her to find out if anything was wrong, he discovered she was feeling hurt. In his rush to get things sorted out, he had not involved her in the discussions and she felt left out. She had always been seen as the irresponsible younger child, whereas Jack was trusted with important tasks from a young age.

# Summary

## Step Two ● Going through the options

- It is important to exhaust all the alternatives before deciding to go down the care home route. Look at extra sources of support like adapting the house or looking for alternative housing arrangements first.

- Care homes vary in lots of ways. Some provide personal care, others nursing. Some are registered to care for particular needs, such as dementia or mental health problems. Some are purpose-built, others converted old buildings. Think about the kind of home your relative will need and prefer.

- Older people settle better if they feel involved in the process of selecting a home. Talk with them about their wishes, should they ever need to go into a home, as a way to help them prepare psychologically.

- Involving the wider family and friends, though time-consuming and potentially fraught, is important. Secure agreement when the need arises to find a home.

# Step Three
# Making financial plans

At this stage, having considered all the alternatives, you may think that the best place for your relative to live is a care home. You have thought through ways of getting them more help at home, options for adapting their home or moving them to more suitable housing, but this may not be enough to meet their growing needs for care and support.

Before you move on to looking at the homes available, you need to be aware of the financial processes involved. This will inform your search and help you prepare for the steps that will be needed in the future.

## First things first – what is an assessment and why is it important?

An important part of finding the right care home for anyone is having their needs addressed. Without knowing what their needs are you can't be sure that a particular home can provide your relative with the care they need. Everyone is entitled to a free assessment from the local authority whether their care home will be funded privately or not. Your relative is also entitled to a free means-tested financial assessment to see how much, if anything, they have to contribute to their care costs.

## The role of social services in assessing need and how to contact them

When you are looking for an assessment start with your local social services. They are often based in the town hall. Ask for the care management team as it is a care manager who will assess your situation. The role of social services is to make a detailed assessment of your relative's community care needs and then arrange support you may need at home or recommend you look at care homes. Even if your relative has been assessed in the past, needs change over time.

## Preparing for assessment by social services care manager

When the care manager visits, they will ask certain questions to help them work out how much support your relative needs. The assessment is designed to be 'person-centred' with everything stemming from the client's presenting needs, wishes and aims. To prepare for their visit, think through which of the 'activities of daily living' are a struggle. Look back over recent months to identify changes. Calculate how much time you, and others, spend each day supporting your relative. Analyse ways they may be at risk living at home and the effect their needs are having on neighbours and the wider family. Often, the older person will 'rise to the occasion' and present a capable image to the care manager when they visit. Your reports of their needs are an important part of the assessment process.

## What to do if obtaining an assessment is difficult – your rights

Obtaining an assessment may not be easy. Social services departments struggle to respond to all the requests for assessment. Older people with relatives supporting them may not be seen as being in such urgent need. However, although there may be waiting lists of people needing assessment, your relative is likely to be eligible for an assessment under the low-threshold, broad responsibilities local authorities carry under the law. Risks to a person's independence form part of establishing the need for assessment, so mention anything you feel may undermine your relative's ability to live independently. Remember, if you are providing a significant level of care and support for your relative, you are also entitled to have your own needs assessed separately at the same time their needs are being assessed. Contact Carers UK (www.carersuk.org.uk) for information about carers' assessments.

## What about assessment and choosing a home if my relative is in hospital?

Your relative may be moving to a care home from hospital. They may have had an illness like a stroke. Perhaps there was an accident, such as a fall. Maybe while in hospital, it became clear that they would not be able to return home and you were advised to look for a care home. Hospitals have social workers, or care managers, working with families in these situations. Their job is to make sure the person can be safely discharged, either back home, or to another place where they can be cared for. They will advise on what needs to happen next to arrange for the older person to leave hospital.

Social services can be fined if they do not arrange for an older person to be discharged once medical staff have decided they are ready to move on. You may have heard the unfortunate term 'bed-blocking' to describe a person who no longer needs a hospital bed. Another term used is 'delayed discharge'. For each day they are in a bed after doctors say they can leave, social services are charged a fee. This means care managers are under pressure to sort out a place in a care home, even if only on a temporary basis, while the person waits for a space in their first choice of home to become available. Choosing a care home is a crucial decision – it could be the person's home until they die and it is important they feel safe and happy there.

Having to move twice is stressful for a frail older person so should be avoided if possible. Older people have a right to choose where they live and they cannot be put in a care home against their wishes (unless under the Mental Health Act or National Assistance Act). If you believe the home your relative has been offered will not meet their needs, be calm but firm in speaking on their behalf. If necessary, take advice from the organisations listed at the end of the book.

> Celia was under pressure to arrange for her sister, Martha, to leave hospital. She was not well enough to return to her council house. Celia had spoken with Martha and knew which care home she wanted. It was a home Martha knew, as she had visited one of her former neighbours there. Although the fees were within what social services were willing to pay, it was a popular home and there were no rooms free. Should Martha hold out to stay in hospital until a place became available? Or should she move temporarily in to a different home in the neighbourhood that she doesn't know but has a vacancy?

## What care does the NHS provide free of charge?

### Fully funded continuing NHS health care in a care home

Some residents are eligible to have their care fully funded by the NHS in a care home if they meet certain eligibility criteria. New national criteria were introduced in October 2007 but before that there were variations across the UK because each area had its own criteria. Some areas have interpreted eligibility for NHS continuing care very narrowly. In other areas more people qualify. Generally speaking, to meet the criteria for having all your costs met by the NHS, you have to have complex and fluctuating healthcare needs and a high level of dependency. People have a right to have their possible need for fully funded care assessed by the appropriate team. The shorter, checklist screening tool can show if a person needs the full assessment. If you are not happy with the outcome, there are rights to have the decision reviewed.

### Intermediate care

This is a short period of care (usually six weeks) when you have been in hospital or to avoid you having to go into hospital. It can be available for up to six weeks, free of charge, and is based around a care plan designed to maximise a person's independence. The aim is to enable a person to return to their own home after hospital treatment, or (by providing suitable services) to avoid the need for hospital admission.

### Care provided by registered nurses in care homes

If your relative is assessed as needing care in a home which provides nursing, the part of the care provided by the qualified nurses in the home will be funded by the NHS with that element of their fees covered by the Registered Nursing Care Contribution. Your relative will be assessed by the NHS as eligible for this contribution. The contribution does not cover the help staff give with personal care in England, though this part of the fees is covered in Scotland if your relative is 65 or over and up to a limit of £149 per week. The NHS contribution is paid directly to the care home and this should be reflected in the fees your relative or the local authority pays. Currently, the rate of this contribution in England is £101 per week but it is normally reviewed on an annual basis. The rates differ in Wales, Northern Ireland and Scotland (where they are paid for by the local authority).

### Continence services

Just as if they were still living at home, your relative is entitled to continence advice from a specialist nurse and to continence supplies such as pads, if they are assessed as requiring this help.

### Other NHS support

This includes chiropody, physiotherapy or equipment, including pressure relief mattresses, mobility or communication aids. If your relative has been admitted to hospital for assessment and treatment under Section 3 of the Mental Health Act 1983, then on discharge they would automatically be entitled to free aftercare under Section 117 of the same Act which can include the full cost of a care home placement.

## If my relative does not qualify for free NHS care, can they get help with the cost from social services?

The system for working out if your relative can have help with the cost of paying for a care home is based on a 'means test', in effect how much money they have, including the value of their home if they own it. At the time of writing this book, if you have over £22,250 in capital assets, you have to pay the full cost of the fees in the care home, minus any nursing contribution you are assessed as being eligible for. When your money falls to £22,250 you start to get help from social services, though you will still be paying part of the fees.

When it falls to £13,000 social services will pay their maximum contribution up to their standard rate with you contributing just your income. Your state pension and any benefits to which you are entitled will be going towards the cost. They must, however, leave you with what is called a Personal Expenses Allowance (spending money), currently £21.15 per week, to pay for extra things not covered by the home's fees. For some time, we at Age Concern along with other groups have campaigned to have the Allowance increased because as it stands it leaves older people in a difficult position with very limited opportunities to pursue a fulfilling life. Their choices are restricted, for instance in keeping in contact with family and friends.

## So if my relative gets help with the fees from social services, are their choices restricted?

Your relative is entitled to a choice in the home they go into. It can even be in a different local authority area, but social services in the area will be responsible for the funding and have a top limit, a 'normal rate' that they are usually prepared to pay, unless you can show that a more expensive home is the only one that can meet your relative's needs. You can choose a home that has higher fees than the council's standard rate if you are able to pay a '**third party top-up**'. This is usually paid by a relative. You need to be confident that the top-up source will not disappear, as your relative may have to move to another home if they become totally reliant on social services to make up the fees. If the local authority is unable to provide the type of accommodation that they have assessed that they need, they may be obliged to provide this accommodation at a higher cost than their normal/usual cost but only charge the usual rate. It is important that they take full account of a person's psychological and social needs. Local authorities should not set an arbitrary rate for what they are prepared to pay for a care home place if it's not possible to purchase a place in their locality for that rate.

Under the National Assistance Act 1948, spouses are currently liable to maintain each other. However, the Department of Health intends to abolish the liable relative rule and has included this change in the new Health and Social Care Bill, which at the time of writing is progressing through parliament. In recent years, the Department of Health has issued guidance that strongly encourages local authorities not to seek liable relative payments pending the repeal of the rules.

Funding has been made available to authorities to compensate them for any additional costs incurred as a result of not collecting liable relative payments.

If you or your spouse enters a care home and the person remaining at home is asked to make a liable relative payment, raise the points in the preceding paragraphs with the local authority. If the authority still wishes to discuss the possibility of a liable relative payment, please contact us at Age Concern for further advice. If you or your spouse is currently making a liable relative payment, ask the local authority to review this arrangement in view of the Department of Health's guidance and contact us for further advice if the authority indicates it wants the arrangement to continue.

Some charities support residents in meeting their fees by providing a third party top-up, for instance occupational benevolent funds which support people who have worked in a particular profession, trade or industry. Charities like this prefer to give towards fees and cannot be expected to enter into any contractual arrangements with a care home. For more information about the role of charities in supporting individual residents, contact the Association of Charity Officers on 01707 651777.

## What happens if my relative lives with me – can I stay in the house?

The local authority has to 'disregard' a person's home (that is, not make a charge on it) if they share it with:

- a partner (who could be a husband, wife, civil partner or someone they live with as though they were married)
- a relative aged 60 or over
- a relative under 60 who is 'incapacitated'
- a former partner who is a lone parent
- a child under 16 whom they are liable to support.

A person in one of these categories can stay living in the home and its value will not be taken into account. When one of a couple enters a care home on a permanent basis, the local authority has to disregard the resident's interest in their former home for as long as the other spouse or partner remains there. The partner or spouse may at some point wish to move from that property, perhaps to somewhere smaller and more manageable. Once the original property has been sold, the disregard ends and the resident's share of the proceeds could be taken into account in the financial assessment. Government guidance says that, where necessary, residents should be able to use part of their share of the sale proceeds to enable their spouse to buy a more suitable property. Unmarried partners or other relatives benefiting from a disregard should ask to be treated in the same way. The guidance does not specify how any capital remaining after the purchase of the new property should be treated and local authorities have adopted differing approaches to this.

The local authority (but not the Pension Service) also has a discretionary power to ignore the value of any premises where the local authority considers it reasonable to do so. For instance, if it is lived in by someone who does not fit into the above categories, like a younger relative who is not incapacitated but has been helping to look after your relative; or a friend who lives with your relative and is 60 or over. For 12 weeks in the care home (so long as you have been assessed as needing permanent residential accommodation, other capital you have is below £22,250 and your income is insufficient to meet the fees) you can top up your own fees subject to a limit of £13,500.

Even if there is no one else living with your relative, there are alternatives in place so that they need not sell their house. They can set up a 'deferred payment agreement' with the local authority agreeing to provide funding on a loan basis, to be repaid when the property is sold at a later date.

The local authority has discretion over whether or not they enter into this agreement on a case by case basis. The agreement stands until the date your relative ends it (for example, because they have sold the house) or until 56 days after they die. Your relative will be given the agreement in writing, and, if turned down by the authority for deferred payment, they can ask for a written explanation of the reason they were refused. It is important to look into all the options with the help of expert advice. Things like entitlement to Pension Credits are affected by the value of property.

Another way of avoiding selling the house is if your relative rents it out and uses the rental to pay the care home fees. Your relative's home is disregarded in the first twelve weeks of them being in a home. There is no need to rush into selling the property and it is well worth the effort of seeking specialist advice on achieving an income to cover care home fees.

## How will my income and capital be affected by my relative going into a care home?

If it is your partner and their pension which is used to cover the cost of fees, you may have concerns about how your income will be affected, especially if their income is higher than yours. When one partner in a marriage or civil partnership enters a care home, 50% of that person's occupational pension, personal pension or payment from a retirement annuity contract can be passed back to the person remaining at home. For unmarried couples, the local authority has the discretion to make income available to the partner remaining at home by increasing the resident's personal expenses allowance. The partner remaining at home (subject to their income and capital status) might qualify for Pension Credit or other means tested help.

## What if my relative cannot manage their own finances?

There are provisions for people who have difficulty managing their finances which allow another person to take over. An older person can nominate a relative or friend to look after their affairs should they reach a point when they are unable to do so. The old term for this arrangement was 'Enduring Power of Attorney' and if made before 1 October, 2007 EPA can still be used whether or not it has been registered. In 2007, the law changed and the person concerned must now ask for 'Lasting Power of Attorney' (LPA) (see the last section of this chapter concerning The Mental Capacity Act).

43

Under the new lasting power of attorney, relatives (or others) can be given responsibility not only for financial decisions, but also for involvement in care and health decisions. It is best to register as attorney as early as possible. Contact the Office of the Public Guardian on 0845 330 2900 (www.publicguardian.gov.uk) to find out what you need to do next. If it is too late for your relative to give you responsibility for their finances because they no longer have the capacity to understand the nature of an LPA, you may need to take on this role via the Court of Protection. This involves a lot more paperwork and accountability.

Your relative may already have a solicitor they know and trust but there is, in addition to a general solicitor, a specialist organisation called Solicitors for the Elderly (SFE) (see **Appendix 2**). They can recommend a solicitor to advise on the steps you need to take. Generally a sensitive solicitor, such as a SFE member, will insist on seeing the older person by themselves to ensure their interests are protected. They have produced a leaflet, 'Why am I left in the waiting room', which explains why this is the case. It is understood that, quite often, a family will consider that their affairs are intermingled and they only have one agenda.

Specialist solicitors are trained to take time and use the best methods available to communicate with an older person who may have disabilities. For instance, a well-known device to communicate with people suffering from a form of Aphasia where there is an inability to recognise words, is to draw diagrams. These may use simple pictures, but make it clear. The older person can nod and agree to the appropriate decision.

For complex financial advice over meeting care costs, it is wise to consult specialist financial advisers. They will have taken exams in long term care set by the Financial Services Authority to establish competence in this very complex area, especially as it relates to safeguarding and maximising savings, investments and understanding Immediate Need Care Fee Payment Plans, or any other aspect of funding concerns. Financial advice can enable your relative to identify whether their accommodation is affordable over the long term and the consequences of running out of money and being in a home which is inappropriate for the assessed needs or more expensive than the local authority would fund. These issues can be addressed with the local authority and the care home at the outset if the financial situation is known.

If you are self-funding your care, attendance allowance is payable to help with the cost of fees. This is currently £44.85 per week if you need care by day *or* by night, or £67.00 if you need care by day *and* night. If the local authority is funding your care, attendance allowance stops after four weeks unless you have deferred payments and will be paying the LA back.

## What steps are there for those being funded by social services?

### ❶ Being assessed

You will first need to have care needs assessed. This will influence the type of home to choose. After the social services care manager has carried out the care needs assessment, they will arrange for a social services financial assessment. This is to work out how much the resident will be contributing to the care home costs.

### ❷ Choosing a home

Once it has been established that your relative needs to be cared for in a care home and that social services will be helping with the fees, you will be asked to look at local homes. Social services should tell you the level of fees they are willing to pay and may give you a list of homes that fall into this bracket. They will also give you details of the assessed care needs so you can work out which homes on the list may be suitable. You can then look at suitable homes and find out if the ones you think will suit your relative have a vacancy. There is limited advice and support for self-funders in looking for a home. This was highlighted in the Commission for Social Care Inspection's (to be called the Care Quality Commission as of April 2009) annual report, *The State of Social Care in England 2006/07*, which noted the disparity of experience between those who receive a service and those left to arrange care largely or totally by themselves.

### ❸ How the placement is arranged

Social services need to be involved in the process of placing your relative if they are going to fund the place. Your care manager will contact the care home to arrange the placement, but your relative needs to make sure you are happy with the plans. The care home's contract will be with the local authority but you should be given details of what it includes.

## ❹ Homes in which social services departments have contracted beds

Some homes in your area may have several (even all) beds which are managed by the local social services department. Social services control who goes into these beds. Historically, these homes are often ones that were run by social services, but which were taken over in the last 15 years by another organisation (a charity or private company). They will now run them in partnership with social services. Social services commission specific services and closely monitor the care provided. They make regular visits to ensure the home is following the contract that was jointly agreed. You can only get one of these places if social services allocate it and their decisions are based on local needs. Social services have beds that provide nursing care as well as personal care, whereas in the past social services tended to specialise in homes providing personal care. Your choice of care home does not have to be restricted to these block booked beds.

## ❺ Panel decisions over funding

Social services departments hold regular meetings to decide whose care should be funded in a care home and to allocate any beds they have in local care homes. If several people need a limited number of beds, they will see whose needs are greatest and take a number of factors into consideration.

## ❻ What if you cannot find a place in a home within social services' funding limit?

You should be happy that a care home will meet your relative's needs before you agree to a placement. No home is perfect, but you need to feel confident that most things are right for your relative. If there are no places available at the price you have been given by social services, or no homes able to meet your relative's needs, social services have an obligation to pay a higher level. If you do not like the homes that have a vacancy at the right price, you have the option of making a third party top-up to make up the difference. The local authority would have to satisfy itself that the top-up can be afforded by the third party for the duration of your relative's stay in the care home.

Your relative is not permitted to top up the fees themselves from their remaining capital except under the 12 week property disregard funding arrangements mentioned above, or under a deferred payments agreement. Usually, social services would pay the home the full amount and invoice you for the top-up.

At the moment care home owners operate differential pricing and cross-subsidising to make up for local authorities paying rates too low to cover costs (within tight funding provision by central government). This, in effect, can mean self-funding residents subsidise those funded by the local authority. You have the right not to be asked to top up, except where you choose a care home that is more expensive than the usual cost.

## ❼ Trial periods

The first three months your relative is in a care home is considered a 'trial period'. They are not committed to staying in the home and the home is not committed to keeping them. At the end of the trial period, the situation will be reviewed to see if it is going well from everyone's point of view.

## ❽ Placing the person in another area – who funds? What other issues are there?

Even if your relative is entitled to help from social services with care home fees, they do not have to stay where they have been living. People sometimes move to a care home where family will be able to visit more frequently and social services can fund a place in another area. You may have difficulty if you are suggesting moving the person to a place where care home fees are much higher than their current home.

## What steps are there for those funding their own care?

## ❶ Being assessed

Even if your relative is likely to pay their own fees, it is still important to have care needs assessed to look at all the other options and help determine the type of home needed and whether the NHS should be responsible. Following on from the care needs assessment, the social services financial assessment will confirm if your relative is to be self-funding.

## ❷ Choosing a home

Social services may give you a list of homes to look at, based on the care needs assessment. Alternatively, you could obtain this from the registration body CSGI (to be called the Care Quality Commission as of April 2009) or from EAC (Elderly Accommodation Counsel). You will have to calculate the level of fees your relative can afford based on how long their capital will last. If they only have a limited budget and you choose a home significantly beyond what social services normally pay, your relative may have to move to another home when their own money runs out.

## ❸ Requesting a place

Once you have chosen a home, you can make a direct request to the home for a place, or to go on a waiting list if your relative is self-funding. The contract will be between your relative, if they have capacity (or a member of the family if they do not), and the care home.

## ❹ Signing the contract

Read the contract carefully before you sign it. Ideally, if the placement is not an emergency, you should read it before your relative moves in. The contract should specify:

- basis of the stay (that is, permanent or temporary)
- details of the resident's room
- care and services provided, for example meals/laundry
- who is responsible for paying the fees
- what the fees are, how they are calculated and when they are paid
- extra services not covered in the fees that may be charged for
- residents' rights and entitlements
- the care home's rights and obligations
- how to make a complaint
- period of notice to move out of the home or terminate the contract
- what the resident will be charged to hold the room if they are away for any reason
- how the home will meet special needs, for example, dietary and religious
- how changing care needs will be managed
- insurance and security for residents' money and valuables
- details of the home's liability insurance.

If you have any doubts about the terms of contract contact the Citizens Advice Bureau locally or trading standards for legal advice, or look at *Care Homes for Older People: National Minimum Standards*, and the Care Home Regulations, which are based on the Care Standards Act 2000. The Office of Fair Trading (OFT) have produced a leaflet about unfair terms and conditions in care homes.

## ⑤ Trial periods

As with local authority funded people, the first three months your relative is in a care home is usually considered a 'trial period'. At the end, your relative's situation will be reviewed to see if everyone is happy with the placement.

## What does the new Mental Capacity Act say about decision-making?

The new Mental Capacity Act, which came into force in 2007, is designed to help professionals and family members support a person who might have difficulty making decisions for themselves because of conditions like dementia. It sets out how to assess whether a person can or cannot decide. Then, if you have 'reasonable belief' they are unable to make a decision, it advises how to make that decision on their behalf.

The Mental Capacity Act is a positive development for people with dementia. They have often had decision making taken away from them too quickly. This legislation says:

- we must assume a person has capacity unless we can prove otherwise
- we should give a person support in making decisions
- we should not treat a person as incapable of making decisions because they make what we might consider unwise or eccentric decisions
- if we have to decide for someone, we must try to do so in their 'best interests'
- before deciding for a person, we must ask ourselves if the outcome could be achieved in a less restrictive way.

As a relative, you may be affected by the Act in two ways. Firstly, you might have to talk to professionals, such as doctors, about whether you feel the person is able to decide for themselves.

Secondly, you might be the person making decisions for a person. To do this, you need to have a 'reasonable belief' they lack capacity to make decisions. You have to take each decision, large or small, on a case by case basis. With some decisions, and at certain times, your relative may be able to decide for themselves, but in other cases they may not. These questions will help you decide if your relative has the capacity to make decisions, in each situation that arises:

- do they have a general understanding of what decision needs to be made?
- do they understand the consequences of the decision?
- can they weigh up this information and use it to make the decision?
- can you assist them, in any way, in making their own decision?
- can you help them communicate their decision, wishes or feelings?

In care homes, staff need to support residents in making decisions, too. Staff also have to document this 'consent'. Consent is about being sure that the resident is able to give permission for any treatment, intervention or activity before it takes place and at regular intervals if there is an ongoing matter. All matters which affect the resident should be discussed with them so that they are fully informed about the choices available. Any individual's refusal or withdrawal of consent should be accepted, unless they lack capacity. Even when a resident lacks capacity, options should be presented in imaginative ways to promote choices and decision making where possible. Friends and family members can support the resident's decision making as they know the person well. They understand decisions and choices they made in the past before their capacity was diminished.

'Making Decisions: A guide for family, friends and other unpaid carers' is a booklet about the new Mental Capacity Act produced by the Ministry of Justice. (You can download it at www.justice.gov.uk, or ring 0238 087 8038 for a hard copy.)

# Summary

## Step Three ● Make your financial plans

- If you have good reason to believe your relative may need to move into a care home, ask for their needs to be assessed by your local social services department. Do this even if it is likely they will be paying for their own care.

- Speak to organisations and individuals who can give best advice on your legal and financial situation before going ahead with big decisions that will influence your relative's future.

- Make sure you are clear on the financial and contractual details when considering a place in a home. If your relative will be a 'self-funder', check the small print and seek advice if anything is unclear. If social services are contributing, you should still be fully informed of the financial arrangements.

- The new Mental Capacity Act gives clear guidance on helping a person who might struggle to make decisions for themselves. Before helping with a decision on behalf of your relative, involve them fully in discussing the options and check that the option you are choosing is in their best interests.

# Step Four
# Start looking

By this stage, you and your relative will have decided that a care home is right for them and have a broad idea of the type of home and the priorities most suited to them. This chapter will help you to identify or refine your choice and understand the range of care options within care homes most suited to their needs. It will help you to involve and prepare your relative for the changes ahead.

There is a comprehensive section on the visit with checklists. The specialist needs of people with dementia will be given a focus with some simple observations and tips to help you know what to look for, including the most important things for people living in a care home.

# Decision making

You may have already:

- contacted your local social services to assess your relative's needs, and discussed various options. Although your relative may have more than £22,250 in capital, you are entitled to this assessment anyway. This is the threshold for the amount of capital they possess above which they will need to pay full care home fees

- been in touch with the GP for support and a medical assessment of their needs

- been in touch with charities and/or other organisations (See **Appendix 2**) to investigate the alternatives from their comprehensive databases such as the Elderly Accommodation Council (EAC)

- investigated other alternatives such as extra care housing

- considered your priorities and type of care home required (for example, one that provides personal care, care with nursing or any speciality such as dementia care). You may have decided to look for a specialist home for a religious or particular occupational group or 'community of interest'

- found out what is available in the locality you have decided on.

# Knowing where to look

Whatever advice or hearsay you pick up about a particular care home, it is always best to experience it for yourself. Assuming that you already know the type of home you need, you can start looking. You will soon find that each care home has its own identity. If you have time to view several places, you will feel more confident in your eventual decision. Remember, it could be your relative's home for some time. If a home is popular you might decide that joining a waiting list is the best option.

### Directories and websites

Your local social services and organisations such as Care Choices (01223 207770 or www.caredirections.co.uk) provide directories covering the area you are looking. Care Choices provides information on choosing a care home or care agency and other options with valuable information including financial planning, hospital discharge procedures and Lasting Powers of Attorney. You may also find it useful to contact FirstStop who provide free information and advice about care in later life (0800 377 7070 or www.firststopcareadvice.org.uk).

# The Inspectorate

The Commission for Social Care Inspection (CSCI) (to be called the Care Quality Commission as of April 2008) provides a list of care homes in the area you are looking. They also provide the inspection reports to go with them on their website. Care homes are inspected according to their quality and safety. There are standards that all care homes have to abide by and are inspected against. These include:

● people's rights to privacy
● dignity
● staff handling medicines
● heating and lighting levels
● money
● the type of care delivered.

The regulator's role is to protect residents from unjustifiable cost increases and inadequate notice of closure. You can find a home on the CSCI website – www.csci.org.uk – and at www.cqc.org.uk from 2009.

Use the website to find a care home, see an inspection report, share concerns and complaints, or see the new council star ratings. The new quality ratings were introduced in 2008 so that people can see how the services compare on the website. They look like this:

3 star ★★★ Excellent
2 star ★★ Good
1 star ★ Adequate
0 star Poor

The website provides a series of options to help guide you. To find a specific report, identify the type of home or type of service you require, the post code area or a specific home. It will come up with several reports. Read back over them to see if there are any trends. Has the manager been replaced? How have things been put right after a previous inspection? You can request a hard copy of the report from your regional centre. These reports measure a set of previous government minimum standards which are currently being reviewed against criteria which highlight the perspective of the service user. These are known as outcomes. In the future, there will be other ways of judging the quality of care homes. They will help the consumer decide the extent to which home is centred on what residents want to experience in a care home.

Meanwhile some other examples include:

- www.whereforcare.co.uk. This independent website is a ratings and information resource based on how others rated a facility. It provides information and advice (from how care will be funded to questions to ask) for those looking for a care home. It reviews and lists over 20,000 care homes across the UK and Northern Ireland.

- The Registered Nursing Home Association (0121 451 1088) provides a list of registered nursing homes and a list of homes in your area, within their membership: www.rnha.co.uk.

- The National Care Association (020 7831 7090) is another membership organisation which can provide a list of responsibly managed care homes within their membership.

**The inspection process**

Regulation processes are subject to change and the recent changes to inspections mean that although services are assessed according to their quality and safety. More focus is put on homes which have the most problems. There are different types of unannounced inspections: 'key inspections', 'random inspections' (short and targeted on an issue or complaint) or 'themed inspections' (focusing on a specific issue or to look at trends). A key inspection is the most thorough. It looks at how a service is performing, takes into account views and complaints if received, and states what the services do well and improvements they need to make. Reports do not publish the responses of the care home. Ideally, you should be directed to the home's website. This may contain their response. Alternatively, you can request a hard copy of their response from the inspectorate.

**Inspection reports**

It is important that you get as much background information on a care home as possible. Assess the quality and whether or not it is appropriate for your relative. Inspection reports are, by their nature, not only an assessment of some of the elements of care but can also be quite subjective: each individual inspector views quality in a different way. So see if the home meets *your* quality requirements rather than solely relying on the views of other people. They are not the only source of information about the home and the inspections are a snapshot in time.

### NHS or social services

Statutory bodies can only provide a 'signposting' service without giving advice. Social services can provide a list of homes in your area. Even if you are self-funding, it would be beneficial to request an assessment of needs, particularly for those who have limited family support.

### Voluntary sector assistance

There are numerous voluntary organisations available to help you. Many of these are listed in the **Appendix 2**.

## Involving the older person

It's impossible to give clear guidelines about how to involve your relative in looking for a care home: you alone know their situation and needs. Several factors limit the involvement of older people in choosing a care home. They may be too unwell and living with severe disability. They may be less aware of the situation and reasons for looking for a home. Or perhaps the process seems stressful and they would rather trust your judgement and leave the planning to you. Unless your relative lacks capacity, it is ultimately their decision.

However, older people who have felt part of the process of decision making settle better in homes, because they feel they made a positive choice and have control over decisions. Your relative may not be able or willing to be involved in all aspects of the choosing, but may still like to join in discussions, look at literature, or visit some of the homes on your list.

## Seeking their views, wishes and permission to act on their behalf

It is tempting to take over if we see a person we care about struggling to manage even if we do this with the best motives. Discuss the role they would like you to have, this is an important part of respecting their right to be involved. If they can remember the conversation when you asked their permission to act on their behalf, it will help them to accept choices and decisions. It might not always be easy to consult your relative as choices arise, but you will feel more secure in the decisions made if you talk with them about options. Be sensitive when you bring this up.

Most care homes have printed literature that tells you something about the home, and may have photos of the building and activities that go on. There are also inspection reports which some older people going into homes would be able to read and digest. If you are not able to take your relative with you to view homes, you might ask permission to take photographs of the building, facilities and garden. See if there is a newsletter produced by the home. This might give your relative a feel for the place.

## Taking them to view homes and talking through what the move means

There are plenty of reasons for not taking your relative with you to view a home. It might be distressing for them or they might not cope easily with the visit. This is another reason for thinking ahead. Look at homes before the need for full-time care arises.

Moving home under any circumstances is taxing. To do so when you are frail and possibly confused is even more so. Having time to prepare psychologically helps. Talking about what moving to a care home will be like can be part of this preparation. It may be a difficult conversation to have but consider the benefits for your relative of having the opportunity to voice fears and concerns. They can better prepare themselves for what lies ahead.

## Ethical considerations

Some older people in care homes may believe they were not told what was happening to them, which would be against their human rights. However, many have forgotten hours of complex deliberations due to their memory difficulties. Either way if they did not know they were going into a home permanently they may feel betrayed. They may view the family selling their home as being 'behind their back'. Those with memory problems may not recall the events building up to them coming into a home. Some are genuinely misled for a variety of reasons. Relatives sometimes feel too guilty to talk openly about what is happening or they may fear the person will resist coming into a home for good so they tell them they are there for a 'holiday'. This is difficult territory ethically. It can harm relationships in families if an older member feels they have been deceived and betrayed, and it can be harder for them to settle in.

It is especially difficult for families trying to find a home for an older person with dementia. Their capacity to understand why a care home is needed is affected by the disability.

They may not recognise that they are struggling to cope at home. Because of the dementia, they may already live with a high degree of fear and suspicion. They lack the full power to make rational choices based on information given. Family members will need to support the person in making decisions but then feel badly about this. They may even face hostility and blame for pursuing the search for a care home. It takes longer to prepare relatives with a memory disability, but people with dementia can become accustomed to new people and a new environment. Taking the time to familiarise before they are admitted may really pay off.

## Thinking ahead

### Future needs

Try to anticipate what lies ahead. You may feel confident a home can meet their needs at the moment, but will this be the case in a year or two's time? Do you know enough, health wise, to be able to anticipate needs that might arise in the future? Will they be able to stay in the home if they become less mobile, for instance?

Think through important relationships. Will older friends and relatives be able to visit or would the journey become difficult if they became frailer?

### What do most residents want when living in a care home?

Evidence shows that having staff who treat residents as individuals is the most important thing for a resident in a care home. This enables them to:

- have control over decisions about care to the extent of their capabilities
- decide whether they are able to participate in meaningful activities compatible with lifestyle, interests, enjoyment and capabilities
- influence meals, food and drinks
- have their spiritual and religious needs met
- resolve concerns and complaints without fear of retaliation from anyone.

Hurtley and Duff (2005) Relationships Care Community Home Standard.

These aspects need to be experienced as part of a relationship triangle with residents, staff and relatives working as partners.

Most people want to feel a sense of:

- **security** – to feel safe to receive or deliver competent and sensitive care
- **continuity** – recognition of biography, using the past to make sense of the present and help to plan for the future
- **belonging** – providing opportunities to form meaningful relationships or to feel part of a team
- **purpose** – providing opportunities to engage in purposeful activity, or having a clear set of goals to aim for
- **fulfilment** – achieving meaningful or valued goals and feeling satisfied with their efforts
- **significance** – to feel that you, and what you do, matter and that you are valued as a person.

From Nolan (1997) *The Senses Framework*.

See My Home Life website (www.myhomelife.org.uk) for more information.

It is also useful to consider how homes:

- find ways to maintain individuality
- help residents to settle in and fit into a caring community
- have a range of possibilities for meaningful activity and engagement
- involve residents in decision making about the things that matter to them
- help residents to receive the right type of care with access to appropriate health professionals
- show positive leadership and clear lines of responsibility
- have a culture that aims to enhance quality of life.

## The visit

## Getting information about the home

List your priorities considering whether the location is accessible for visiting, the type of social culture, lifestyle and activities provided are appropriate, the suitability of the accommodation and specialist care. You should be offered information about the services provided by the home when you make contact.

Once you have a range of possible homes to look at, select a few. Visit each, talk to the manager or owner and tour the establishment. If you have limited time, you might need help and advice from an independent care adviser. In the ideal situation, once you have visited a few homes, you can examine your shortlist of best options in more depth.

### Short checklist

● Can you see a copy of the Statement of Purpose? This is the official document explaining services, setting out aims, objectives and the philosophy of care. Or ask for the Service User Guide which should be easier to understand.

● How much involvement do the resident and family have in the 'care plan'? This sets out their individual needs, such as the use of specialist equipment, diet or medication, daily life, interests/lifestyle and life story.

● Does the review of care plans (every six months) involve residents and relatives?

● Is a written service user contract/agreement outlining the terms and conditions given on arrival? What do the fees cover? Are there any extras you might be expected to pay for and who will provide the toiletries? What about other sundries or extras such as newspapers, hairdressing, chiropody or therapy?

● Find out the level of security. Might your relative be asked to leave at short notice? (It is not uncommon for homes to change hands to another care provider.)

● What is the admission process?

● Is there a trial period arrangement? What happens if your relative is unhappy with the home after moving in? What are the notice arrangements?

● Can you change your room if you want to?

● How are the residents' and relatives' views considered? Are there residents' and relatives' forums/groups, discussions or interviews?

● Can family and friends visit when they want to?

● Is there a key worker system? Who is assigned to take particular interest and responsibility for a group of residents?

- Is there regular contact with visiting professionals (physiotherapy, chiropody, occupational therapy, dentist, optician, palliative care teams)? Can your relative keep the same doctor?

- How are people enabled to continue to do things they enjoy and keep mobile?

- How often do residents get outdoors?

- What activities/events/outings are there and how often do they take place?

- Is there a quiet area available for more privacy or to receive visitors? Observe whether the atmosphere is friendly. Does it smell fresh? Do the residents seem well turned out, alert and content?

Age Concern can provide you with a free checklist to take with you when you visit a home. Call 0800 00 99 66 or visit www.ageconcern.org.uk for more information.

## Support in looking at homes offered

Looking round care homes can be a daunting experience. Even the practicalities of transport and finding the homes can be challenging, not to mention issues to consider if you are taking your relative along with you. You might need to find someone to look after them while you make your visit. Asking the right questions, and looking out for important aspects of life in the home when you may be feeling upset means it can be useful to have a friend or relative to help. Two pairs of eyes and ears are better than one. Do you have a close friend or family member whose judgement you trust and who may be willing to visit homes with you? Perhaps there is a local charity (like the local Carers Centre, Age Concern or Alzheimer's Society branch) which could support you. Discuss the kinds of questions and observations that are important to you with whoever is helping you. They can prompt you and make sure you get the most out of visits.

Elaine felt insecure as so many of her friends were asking why she didn't move her mother Mary into a home nearby. It would be so much easier to see her regularly if she was just down the road rather than having to make the 80 mile round-trip. Elaine felt it was right to keep her mother local to the area she had lived in all her life. It was especially important Mary kept in touch with her neighbours, Tom and Judy.

They had been so good to her over the years and were almost like another daughter and son, though it pained Elaine to think of it like that. Tom and Judy had a disabled son they looked after at home, so it would be very difficult for them to travel to see Mary. In the same area, Elaine knew they would pop in regularly and that this would make a big difference to Mary. Although the travelling was tiring and time-consuming, Elaine felt it was fairer to carry on rather than risk her mum being cut off from people who mattered to her.

Taking decisions on behalf of another person is a big responsibility. Feeling inadequate or anxious about making the right choices is quite normal. It helps to take a matter-of-fact approach. If you don't understand the terms of language used when you visit, ask for clarification. It is easy for care professionals to use professional jargon which is unfamiliar and daunting. A 'care plan', for example, is a completely alien concept to people who have never had any experience in a care setting. An 'activity co-ordinator' might sound like a strange job if you don't know what it means. Ask questions. It is quite normal for people to need explanations.

## Viewing the home

Keeping a checklist and clear focus of priorities may be helpful. Visiting unfamiliar places is tiring. Allow enough time to reflect after each visit and go through the checklist again, rating each home against criteria you have highlighted. Or you might prefer to jot down key impressions to help when you come to the final analysis of homes worth revisiting.

Spot visits are important before you finally decide on a home. Arrive unannounced and use this opportunity to observe general aspects of the home which you believe are important and relevant to your relative. Highlight the key things of importance according to your relative's priorities. Observing at mealtimes is a good indicator of the quality of experience for a resident. It can be rushed and regimented or an enjoyable part of the day. Is there attention to detail and the right level of help in a dignified way?

The interplay of the atmosphere, layout and the general feel of the place all contribute to how a community works. You want a home to provide a sense of security and continuity, to enable a smooth transition.

Think about:

- physical layout – design, space, colour and lighting
- general organisation – policy, ratio of staff, resources, leadership style, supervision levels and overall philosophy
- personal life – family, friends and staff relationships
- community – type and social mix of people (age, background, mental state and ethnicity) and social atmosphere
- culture – values and attitudes of the staff, and relationships between residents, staff and relatives
- experience of the residents.

# The detailed checklist

Use this list for your second visit, once you have highlighted the areas which represent your relative's priorities.

An * indicates something that is particularly important for people with dementia.

## Location

- Is the home easy to get to for relatives and friends to visit?
- Do you like the surroundings?
- Is there public transport nearby?
- Is the home close to the local community amenities, such as a pub, church or local shops?
- Are the surroundings noisy or quiet?
- Is there an interesting view or something to watch out of the window?

## The welcome and atmosphere

- How were you greeted when you first arrived?
- Does the home appear homely and welcoming?
- Are staff helpful, polite and friendly?
- Does the home feel fresh, clean and comfortable?
- Are there unpleasant odours?
- Do the staff seem calm or rushed and harassed?
- Are there other residents your relative might get on with?
- Are people left alone waiting to be attended to for long periods?
- How friendly are the relationships between the staff and residents?

## General accommodation

- Is it light or gloomy? (People with sensory loss need good lighting)
- Is it clean? Is there a fresh clean smell?
- Is there a separate dining room?
- Are toilet facilities within easy reach of day areas?
- Is there an accessible call system for emergencies?
- Is furniture well maintained?
- Are there communal rooms both with and without television?
- Is there a choice of communal areas?
- Are there are different types of seating arrangements?
- Are corridors well lit and broken up where possible? *
- Does it have a homely feel with familiar objects, artefacts and furnishings? *
- Does it have an easily accessible stimulating environment with things to see and do? *

## Access/orientation

- Are adaptations adequate to enable residents to move around freely (such as rails, wide spaces, walking aids, ramps and grab rails in the WC, chairs of different heights and sizes)?
- Is there a lift or stair-lift?
- Are all main areas accessible to wheelchair users?
- Is there adequate provision for people with hearing or visual difficulties (such as a loop system for hearing aid users in the day room)?
- Does the home have access to appropriate transport for trips and outings?
- Is it easy to find your way around? Are there signs to help you at decision points? *

## The gardens

- Does it look safe, accessible and secure?
- Are the grounds attractive?
- Is there somewhere to sit that is protected from the elements?
- Are residents encouraged and helped to sit outside?
- Are there interesting features to stimulate interest and enjoy? *

## The bedroom

- Is it big enough?
- How near is it to a lift? Is it easy to get to?
- How many personal possessions can be taken to the rooms?
- Is there enough room to receive visitors comfortably?
- Is it possible to adjust heating, turn a light on or open a window easily?
- Are washing and bathing facilities easily accessible?
- Is there adequate storage space?
- Are rooms decorated to feel different from each other?

Arthur wanted both high standards of caring and a room with a view. He is immobile but enjoys the privacy of his books in his own room. The room he moved to had a large bay window overlooking the park. He could watch people unobtrusively throughout the day from the quiet of his room.

## Lifestyle *

- Can residents choose when they get up or go to sleep?
- How much flexibility is there in the daily routine?
- How are residents involved in the day-to-day running of the home?
- Are there regular outings and/or visits to/from the local community?
- Is there a private/comfortable place to make phone calls?
- How are links with the wider community maintained?
- Can you stay in your own room if you choose to?
- Are pets allowed?
- Are there adequate facilities (hairdressing, chiropody, library or other activities)?
- What are the arrangements for laundry and dry cleaning?
- Are residents accompanied to hospital visits and other appointments?
- What arrangements are made with local GPs?
- Do staff encourage residents to participate in activities they enjoy?
- Is TV and radio use appropriate to wishes of residents?
- Are a range of books (including large print, picture books and so on), music and DVDs available?

## Food and mealtimes *

- How are individual food preferences catered for?
- Are the menus interesting and varied?
- Is there choice in the menu?
- What influence do residents have on the menus?
- Are special dietary needs catered for?
- Is specialist assistance offered for those who need it?
- Can meals be taken in bedrooms as well as the dining area?
- Is food and drink available at times other than mealtimes?
- Can you make yourself a light snack or hot drink?
- Can family members join their relative for a meal?

## Activities and social life *

- Is a member of staff responsible for co-ordinating activities?
- How are activities organised? Who is involved and how often do they occur throughout the week?
- Are activities based on individual interests and needs?
- Do activities reflect the everyday life of residents?
- How are relatives, staff and volunteers encouraged to get involved in the social community of the home?
- What range of activities is provided?
- Are there any visiting services (like a library or shop)?
- Do schools/children play a part in the life of the home?

## Spiritual matters

- How are residents able to pursue their faith and matters of importance to them?
- Is there access to churches and other places of worship?
- Do local religious leaders visit the home?
- Is there a quiet area residents can use to pray or meditate?

## Visiting arrangements *

- Are visitors welcomed any time?
- Is there a quiet place for visitors?
- Do some social events include family members?
- Is there an organised relatives' group so issues can be raised and discussed informally?

## Residents

- Are they at ease interacting with those around them?
- Are they well turned out?
- Do the residents seem relaxed, happy and sociable?
- Are they generally sleepy or do they seem alert and interested in what is going on?
- Would your relative fit in?

## Staff

- Do staff take the time to sit and talk with residents?
- Are they courteous, respectful and polite to residents?
- What is the staff turnover like?
- How many agency staff does the home use?
- Do there seem to be enough staff to attend to the needs of residents requiring attention?
- Is there access to specialist help such as chiropody, physiotherapy and occupational therapy?
- Do staff look clean and appropriately dressed?
- Do staff understand and speak the same language as your relative and is this language spoken between staff when they are on duty?
- What qualifications do they have?
- Do staff look purposeful, interested and happily communicate with residents as they carry out their duties?

## Management

- Does the manager seem friendly and approachable?
- How open is management to suggestions and involvement from the family?
- How is care organised – is it person-centred with particular staff taking responsibility for specific residents' well-being and is the staffing based on needs?

## General

- Can your relative imagine themselves feeling at home?
- Do you think they could get along with other residents?
- Can your relative have a trial period?

## Conditions

- Were you given information about how you/your relative can make a complaint or raise a concern?
- What is the policy on negotiating risk with residents and relatives?
- Is there a secure place where valuables can be kept?
- Does the home take responsibility for insuring residents' possessions?
- What notice must be given if your relative wants to leave?
- What percentage of the fees is kept under what circumstances (for example, death or illness)?
- How will the home keep you involved?

## Finances

- Who owns the home?
- Is it financially stable?
- Is it likely to change ownership?
- Have social services agreed to fund care?
- Is there any difference in the fees? If so, who will pay it?
- Can you/your relative afford the fees?
- How long can you continue to pay them?
- Are fees payable in advance?
- What are the financial arrangements after someone dies?

## Before you make your decision

- Do you feel the home can offer the care your relative needs?
- Can you have a trial period to ensure the home suits your relative's needs?
- Would *you* be happy if you were your relative in this home?
- Will you feel comfortable visiting?

# Summary

## Step Four ● Start looking

● **The right information**: Is additional information available from specialist organisations to help you make decisions?

● **Preparing your relative**: Try to involve your relative wherever possible. How can you think about the experience from their perspective?

● **Fees**: Are they sustainable?

● **Location**: Near to amenities, family or friends?

● **Style of building**: Some people like something very cosy and homely while others prefer a more formal hotel style of living. Is it an older family style building or a modern purpose-built facility? Does it accommodate the equipment needed to care 'behind the scenes'?

● **The room**: Is the space big enough to create a sense of home and personal territory?

● **Atmosphere**: Is there a friendly atmosphere?

● **Other residents**: Is there anyone whom your relative could enjoy getting to know?

● **Staff attitudes**: What are their communication skills like? How long have they worked there?

● **Quality of life/lifestyle**: Are there plenty of opportunities to join in a range of activities, learn a new skill, enjoy gentle social encounters with others and make new friends? Alternatively, your relative may prefer their own company. If so, can they be self-contained and happily surrounded by personal artefacts and books in their own room?

# Step Five
# Preparing for the move

Now you've found a selection of care homes, what comes next? This will partly be governed by the circumstances you are in. If your relative is moving from hospital to a home, the process will vary from that if they were going in straight from home. Their state of health will also influence the pace and process of moving them in. The following sections deal with the likely next steps for you and your relative.

The first task is to secure a place for your relative. There will be lots of things to do to prepare for the move. These include talking with your relative to help them prepare psychologically and packing items they will need in the home. Think about who needs to be informed about the move.

## Liaising with the care home

### Requesting a place

Now you have had a good look round homes in the area, read inspection reports and talked with your relative and other people, you may have a shortlist of preferred homes. If your relative is a self-funder, you can approach the home of your choice whenever you feel ready. If it's a popular home, the sooner they go onto a waiting list the better. If social services are paying, it will be their job to contact the home.

### What if a place is not available?

If you are in a position to wait until a place comes free, that may be fine. But if you are under pressure to settle on a home (especially if your relative is in hospital), it may not be easy to hold out for your first choice. You have two options: either you can find another home as a temporary solution, or you can see if your second choice has a place. Once your relative has settled in a home, they may not want to move again.

### Meeting staff before moving in day and pre-admission assessment

Both you and your relative will benefit from establishing contact with staff in the home prior to the day of their admission. Ideally your relative will be able to visit at least once for a few hours. This will help them to get to know staff while helping staff to assess their needs, to be better prepared to care for them when they move in permanently. Sometimes pre-admission visits are not possible (for example, if your relative is quite poorly and/or in hospital, or they are moving to a home some distance away). An alternative is for staff from the home to visit them. Meeting you and your relative is another way for staff to build up a picture of their needs and gain a sense of how they will need to support them.

Care homes have systems for allocating residents to named members of staff who take a special interest in them. These are called 'key workers' or 'named nurses'. They make sure they have all the clothing and toiletries and special personal things they need and build links with their relatives and friends. Before moving in day, arrange a visit when these people are on duty. They will be involved in early discussions about your relative's care needs and at subsequent review meetings.

## Discussing the room and redecoration

Once you have seen the room your relative will be moving into you will be able to identify if the décor is suitable. Would it benefit from repainting? Is the colour scheme to their liking? Are they happy with the curtains and carpet? If there are changes your relative would like, talk to the manager. It will be much easier to do any work before your relative moves into the home. It is important your relative feels at home in their new setting. The way it is laid out and decorated can help.

Sarah's brother, Joe, kept changing the subject whenever she tried to talk to him about moving into the care home. With his history of mental health problems, she felt he needed an opportunity to talk about what he was going through. But it seemed too painful. When Sarah popped into the home one day to ask staff a few questions, they showed her the room Joe would have. They said it needed repainting and it might be sensible to put in a new carpet and curtains at the same time. Did Joe have any preferences for how he wanted it? Now she had some practical choices for Joe to make, Sarah found it easier to talk to him about the move. Planning the colour scheme for his room made the move real for him. It was a good way to talk about it without having to delve too deeply.

## Written information that the home can provide to guide you

The home has to provide you with a statement of purpose and service user guide. Some homes have guides specifically for relatives and friends or a 'welcome pack'. It is useful to know any 'rules' the home has. All homes will ask you to have electrical items checked on admission, for instance. Some homes take pets; others do not.

## Financial information the home should give you

There has been much campaigning to improve financial information given to older people moving into care. If your relative is self-funded, you should be shown the contract before moving in. On admission, it should be available to check and sign. Charities working with older people moving into care homes (listed at the back) can advise you on what the contract should include. Even if social services are organising fee payment, you should know how the costs are being met.

## Services that are available and ones that will need to be arranged

Most help needed by residents will be provided by the home but:

- you might have to take items to be dry cleaned
- the home may not mend clothing so you will have to do small sewing jobs
- usually, homes can buy toiletries, but some prefer relatives to bring them in
- some homes like relatives to take their resident to medical appointments.

## Will your relative keep their existing GP, dentist, chiropodist and so on?

By law residents are able to choose their GP as they would at home. This has advantages, given that the doctor is likely to know them well. If the home is in another part of town, however, the surgery may not be willing to continue with the service. The home is likely to have links with their local surgery or surgeries, which will make regular visits. One attraction of changing to the home's GP is that they may visit frequently. Staff can request they see your relative on a regular basis if there are concerns. You can also arrange to speak with the GP during a visit. The same principles apply to services like dentistry and chiropody. Will your relative value keeping links with professionals they see presently or prefer the convenience of linking in with the home's regular visiting professionals? Part of this decision will be any charges the home makes for using the services of these professionals. In order to compare benefits, make sure you are clear about any financial implications.

## Preparing your relative

**Helping with feelings of anxiety and loss at the thought of leaving their home**

This is the most important, and the hardest, part of preparing for the move. With all the practical tasks facing you, don't forget the vulnerable person at the centre of all the planning and activity. Focusing on your relative's feelings may be painful, but they need opportunity to talk things through.

Your relative may have moved into their current home quite recently or lived there for decades. What does this home mean to them? Does it hold treasured memories? Will leaving it mean letting go of these connections?

How much is your relative's sense of their identity tied up with their home? What are their neighbours like? Our home gives us a sense of safety and security. The thought of being separated from it generates anxiety. Or maybe it has become an unwelcome burden to your relative over the years. If it holds unhappy memories, they may not be too sad about being parted from it.

If possible, talk about what it will mean to your relative to give up their home. Many older people in care homes have not had the chance to talk through the sense of loss they have over leaving their home behind. Talking is part of the grieving process. As with any loss, you can expect them to have strong feelings. They may be more tearful than usual and find it hard to see the positives. They may express anger and resentment, perhaps towards you. Or they may act as if nothing is happening. Denial can be part of grief.

Talk about how life will change moving to a care home. Exploring all the aspects of life that will change for them will help prepare them. This preparation becomes more difficult if they have dementia. They may not remember discussions from one day to the next. They might struggle to grasp the significance of the change about to take place. While you cannot be sure how much information your relative is able to understand, it is important to be open with them. Families who hold back from talking about plans can later feel guilty for deceiving the person. At some level, your relative may be able to take in what is happening. People with dementia are likely to be more anxious. They may feel especially insecure at the prospect of a change to their normal routine, so will need lots of reassurance.

An older person moving to a home some distance from where they have been living can be tricky. It will be harder to pay visits to the home in advance of the move, so it may be difficult for them to imagine what their new life will be like. If possible, try and take them to the home at least once before the day of the move. Show them the home's literature and photographs of the building and the garden. This will help make it more real for them.

The community psychiatric nurse encouraged Raj to talk about the care home with his mum Ravinder in the weeks before the move. Even when she struggled to understand and remember, each day Raj mentioned aspects of living in a care home. They talked about what lay ahead. Ravinder was confused. She would forget much of the conversation, but reflecting back afterwards Raj was glad he had persevered. She took in more than he realised and seemed calm and composed during the move. She seemed to understand and accept what was happening.

**Discussing and preparing things they will need**

### Clothes

Some people gain weight when they settle in to their home (particularly if they enjoy the food) so avoid buying new clothing in large quantity before your relative moves in. Most laundries wash outfits quickly. If you are selecting clothes:

- label every item of clothing to avoid the hassle of clothing going missing. Permanent marker labels can wash off at high temperatures but the home can advise you
- consider seasonal clothes but bear in mind care homes are often warm places
- elastic waists accommodate weight changes and are comfortable
- clothes need to withstand the high temperatures at which the home will wash them to prevent the spread of infection
- woollens are more difficult to maintain than cotton or synthetic mix fabrics
- avoid clothes which need delicate or hand wash treatment
- pay attention to what people enjoy wearing and feel good in. It is important to retain individuality and a sense of pride in what they wear
- choose clothes that are easy to put on so your relative can stay independent – lightweight and stretch fabrics are good
- provide information for the staff about any strong preferences or favourite clothes
- avoid dry cleaning unless you take responsibility and negotiate specific arrangements with the home (particularly if there might be a continence problem)

- jewellery – special items need to be itemised and discussed regarding security. Some residents choose costume jewellery as it saves them from any worries about security. It is difficult for homes to take responsibility if these items get lost. But it is important to maintain the customary appearance, and all 'fake' jewellery is replaceable. Take photos of precious items taken in so that staff will find it easier to locate them if lost.

- if storage is limited, consider keeping clothes that are out of season in another place until they are needed again.

**Outdoor wear and footwear**

Your relative is likely to be indoors most of the time so a comfortable pair of flat indoor shoes and a pair of slippers that give good support (not mules) will be useful. Loose or flimsy footwear with limited support can cause falls. A sturdy pair or two of well-fitting low-heeled outdoor shoes and a warm coat will enable them to go out into the home's garden and for walks locally. Again, make sure footwear is labelled. There are specialist shoe companies for people with problem or very wide feet.

### Personal pictures, photos and ornaments

The new room arrangement will influence how well your relative settles. Having personal items around them will help them feel at home. Start thinking about which photographs and pictures mean the most to them. Are there items of furniture they will want to take (an armchair or a bookcase, for instance)? Things can get broken or lost in a care home, so it is not advisable to take in items of great value. With photos, it is sensible to take in a copy of the original so it won't be a disaster if it is damaged. Write names of people on the back of the photo so that staff are able to identify them and prompt your relative. With soft furnishings, the home will ask you if fire safety regulations are met. This will be linked with when the item was purchased.

### Books and hobby equipment

There will not be a great deal of space so you will need to be selective. Choose books that have significance for your relative by discussing this with them. For some people a prayer book, Bible or other spiritual text which allows them to pray and reflect will be important. Hobby and craft materials need to be relevant to what the person can do now; otherwise, if they are frail and can no longer engage in the activity (such as fine needlework) it may be a sad reminder of the losses of later life. Bring reminders of their earlier achievements (such as cushions they have embroidered or photographs or certificates). These will provide excellent talking points for staff.

### Electrical items – television, music player

Your relative may have a TV or radio they can take with them into the home but it will need to be checked for electrical safety when you first take it in. This might be a good time to replace it (televisions will soon be entirely digital). If you are buying equipment, think carefully about how user-friendly your choice of gadget will be for an older person. Consider investing in a mobile phone if they can manage one. A computer, adapted telephone or more complex large equipment such as a powered wheelchair will need to be discussed with the manager of the home in terms of access, safe storage, internet connection and maintenance etc.

### Bedding, curtains, cushions

The home is likely to supply bedding, curtains and cushions. But your relative's room will be more personal and homely if they have their own items. A bedspread or duvet cover, a pair of curtains or an attractive cushion may give their room that individual touch that makes it more of a home for them.

### Personal items

If your relative has valuables or something very fragile or delicate, you may need to weigh up the risk. Things can get damaged or go missing. Make a checklist. Take measurements before you move for furniture and everything else to ensure it will fit into the room.

### Items and equipment to maintain independence

The use of specialist equipment (such as adapted cutlery, long reaching 'helping hands' to pick things up from the floor, a long handled comb/brush, or a walking frame with an attached frame bag) can help your relative to keep their belongings close at hand. These can help to maintain independence and dignity and should be labelled.

### Pets

Some care homes are able to take a resident's pet. There is more information about this in the **Appendix 6**.

### Legal and financial arrangements

This stage of the journey involves more legal and financial matters. Think about how fees will be paid to the home. How will you arrange for them to have spending money available at the home? Liaising with their bank and other financial institutions will be necessary, too. This might be the stage to activate financial plans made earlier (such as taking on the power of attorney or implementing insurances).

At this stage, as at every other stage, seek your relative's permission to act on their behalf.

# Informing people who need to know

There will be many people to inform when your relative moves to a care home. Start making a list as soon as possible so that you are prepared when the time comes.

### Extended family and friends

There may be ways in which family members can help in the preparation. By keeping them involved, you are keeping your relative's networks strong. Friends and neighbours can be very important too. You will want these people to stay involved in your relative's life when they move to a home, so let them know what is planned. They may also be able to provide support, particularly in the conversations they have with your relative.

### Service suppliers

There may be gas and electricity companies, telephone service suppliers, the milkman, the Royal Mail, newspaper delivery service, home insurance company, window cleaners, home carers and others to inform.

### Cancelling standing orders and direct debits

Review all regular subscriptions, direct debits, membership and standing charges in the light of changed circumstances. Notify the relevant agencies if the house is being sold or if an adjustment needs to be made (such as changing house insurance to insuring the contents of one room).

### Doctor's surgery

As we discussed earlier, your relative may have the option of keeping their own GP. If this is their wish, make contact with the surgery to find out if it will be possible. If they decide to go with the home's regular GP practice, inform their old surgery.

While driving home from visiting his sister Iris in the home, Bob thought about how the first week had gone. With a jolt, he remembered that he had overlooked an important part of helping Iris settle. He had not informed her old WI friends where she was. Although she had long since given up her active role in the Women's Institute, belonging to the group was an important part of her identity. He knew her old friends would want to stay in touch. Bob resolved to ring several of them as soon as he got home.

# Summary

## Step Five ● Preparing for the move

- Have contingency plans in place in case your first choice does not fit into place (for example, if the home your relative likes best does not have a vacancy).

- To ease the transition, enable your relative to have some contact with the home before moving in day. This might just be popping in briefly on a couple of occasions.

- Make a detailed list of everyone who needs to know your relative's change of address and circumstances. Decide how to inform them.

- Create opportunities for your relative to talk through what the change will mean for them. Allow them to grieve giving up their home.

# Step Six
# Moving in

Moving from their own home to a care home is a major life transition for older people. But with support of the family and staff, good quality of life can be achieved. You can help prevent a sense of dislocation from the past familiar routines, places and people. This all enables a person to feel more in control, maintain their identity, prevent loneliness, boredom and a sense of helplessness during this period. In moving and settling into a new environment, it is possible for people to pick up the threads of living life again, albeit in a new way, with access to support 24 hours a day. There will still be opportunities to experience enjoyment and fulfilment within a different setting. Some older people find living in a care home preferable to their experiences of receiving care in their own home.

Client
Ref. No.

## Getting to know the person

If your relative cannot introduce themselves, outline the 'essence' of the person for the staff – their interests, personality type, preferences and routines. This can help your relative settle in feeling known as an individual. The information can help staff build positive relationships and offers something to talk about as well as contributing to the resident's quality of life. The more information staff have, the better for everyone, as it helps to personalise care. Families and friends can do much to shape this. They can also maintain links with their relative's former life and interests outside the home.

When your relative moves in, you can help them to understand the layout of the home, organise their room, learn what is available to them and where to go for help. You have a significant role in helping ease their orientation by reinforcing information and providing support and encouragement.

## Biography

Help staff get to know your relative's needs by telling them about important aspects of their lives (including notable experiences, events and relationships). This is often done by providing them with a biography. This 'pen portrait' can help staff to have meaningful conversations. They can introduce your relative to other residents if there is something in common. This role is often assisted by an activity co-ordinator if there is one.

Here are some heading suggestions to highlight the type of information that could be useful to the home. Highlight the most important facts.

- Preferred name/use of title
- Place of birth
- Significant places
- Family
- Friends
- School days
- Important life events
- Occupation (first job, training for a profession and any significant experience in working life, awards and so on)
- Personality type
- Social background/interests/networks
- Important values and cultural/religious beliefs

- Pets
- Likes/dislikes (food, pastimes, entertainment, music, TV, radio)
- Activities and hobbies enjoyed
- Skills and talents
- Major events that have had a significant (positive or negative) impact on them

### Making a profile

It is worth using this biography to create a profile of your relative. Bringing the biography to life with additional details about matters can make all the difference to personalised care. For people with memory problems, relatives are 'guardians' of their story.

Some people like to make a book or box containing memorabilia. This can include memory prompts or photographs, CDs or DVDs with family films. Others might put together a 'life collage' with pictures representing significant people, places or events, likes and dislikes in picture format. You can be as imaginative as you like. It can help staff to get to know your relative if you talk about them informally.

Everyday likes and dislikes being known can help people with communication or memory problems. A list might include:

- favourite drinks (hot, cold, alcoholic beverage, daily rituals and how they like drinks served)
- food (likes and dislikes, preferred time of eating, special cutlery requirements and special treats)
- clothing (colour favourites, likes and dislikes and accessories normally worn)
- bed (any rituals around bedtime to assist sleep, nightwear, bedclothes, number of pillows, lighting and ventilation)
- bathing (preferred time, preferred method, items used, likes and dislikes)
- appearance (hair care, skin care, make-up type, colours, nail care, hairdressing frequency and style preferences, aftershave or perfume used)
- companionship likes and dislikes (for example, male and female company, pets and comforters)
- routines/habits (how they like to be woken up in the morning)
- abilities (what they can do for themselves and what they need help with)
- conversation (topics enjoyed)
- touch (likes and dislikes)

- personality type (open and chatty or quiet and reserved)
- visitors (names of family and friends and photographs in the room)
- activities (what a person enjoys doing during the day, where they like to sit, or any particular routines and habits)
- entertainment and interests (music likes, radio/TV, indoor and outdoor)
- key dates and people of significance
- some idea about a former significant carer relationship.

## Personalising rooms

You can help to create a sense of home by using objects and bringing in items that create a meaningful place for your relative. This can help them to continue to enjoy items of significance and remember past achievements and important dimensions of life. They help maintain identity and provide some continuity at a time of loss and change.

Your relative will have access to the public areas of the home and garden but their private space is their room. When 'down sizing' to one room, it is especially important to create a personal space with meaningful associations. Photographs and small items of furniture (depending on the room size and the home's policy) can enhance and transform a bland room into a more homely, personalised one. Room sizes will vary according to the type, style and period of the accommodation. Some people like to have an extra comfy chair for visitors.

For people who have dementia, a memory box or a store of treasured memorabilia, photographs, important documents, favourite music or a film can help them keep in touch with the personal aspects of life. These things provide significant memory prompts.

## Spending money

Having one's own money is important. But if a person lacks capacity, it is up to the discretion of the family, in discussion with the care home, as to how this can be best managed.

Some residents like to have small change on them. It can provide a sense of continuity in the management of their own affairs (for example, paying for their own paper or the hairdresser visiting the home).

It also means they have cash available to pay for things like toiletries, newspapers, hairdressing, chiropody and going out using their own purse/wallet.

Avoid keeping too much cash in your relative's room or handbag. The home will have a safe where it can be kept. They or their key worker can then ask for money as and when they need it. The home's administrator is usually the person responsible for looking after residents' money. They have to keep a record of money that comes in and what is spent. They will supply you with these details and receipts for monies spent on request.

Check how much money your relative has available when you visit as it is awkward if they run out of money. Every individual will have different needs and wishes regarding money. Make sure they have enough and don't need to keep asking for change. If your relative has dementia, depending on the stage and mental capacity, find ways to help them to retain a sense of control, dignity and independence and to feel they have access to the things that are of importance to them. In the case of money, it could be small change in a handbag purse or wallet.

If the local authority is paying fees, there is a basic £21.15 per week Personal Expenses Allowance (PEA) limit for spending money. This can be spent on anything your relative wishes. Otherwise, if it is not used, it is put into a protected bank account. It is not intended to pay for contracted services assessed as necessary. This allowance can cover such items as books, tapes/CDs, clothing, hairdressing, trips, gifts and any extras. £21.45 only covers the 'basics' of life and is not enough to offer people more dignity and choice in their daily lives.

Check whether sundries (from tights to toothpaste) are provided by the home. These are usually charged in a separate invoice. Sometimes it is easier for the home to manage this in house.

## Medication and other services

This is often an area of concern, especially as nursing home residents, on average, can take about six or seven types of medication. There are strict guidelines about practice and how medication is administered at the right time in the right dose with regular review. Many residents change their GPs, particularly if they move out of area. This will also involve a review of medication. Where a resident takes their own medicines there will be a locked drawer or box in the room which they can use themselves.

Care homes can only accept medication if it is in its original dispensed packaging with clear instructions (showing the exact dosage) on the label. Individual blister packs are used to ensure accurate recording and prevent error. There are strict procedures for the receipt, recording and storage and handling of medicines. These must be handled by staff with the appropriate training. Many homes have good relationships with pharmacists who assist them with their systems. Relatives should be informed if there is any change in medication. Some independent residents can be enabled to take responsibility for their own medication where this is possible. All residents should expect the highest standards in the management of their medication. This is particularly important for people needing palliative care or with dementia or communication problems. They are particularly vulnerable to untreated pain, inappropriate prescription of tranquillisers or negative side effects of medication if regular reviews do not take place.

Access to other services (such as specialist nurses who specialise in incontinence, wound care, palliative care and other therapists), if they are not available within the home, may be accessed through the Primary Care Trust (PCT). Availability may vary depending on the local policy. Care homes are sometimes viewed as low priority, despite the level of need.

Some homes employ their own part-time visiting specialists if the local NHS service is inadequate. This may incur additional charges unless it is included as a service within the negotiated fee. Some homes provide additional access to other 'extra' services (such as chiropody or aromatherapy).

## Arranging the move

## The day of the move

Each home will make its own arrangements with you. For someone who is confused and agitated, it might be worth considering the following regime carried out in a home for people with dementia. An adverse reaction is likely when people feel insecure, bewildered and afraid. For anyone, change can be challenging, even if one is well prepared.

The first day in a care home can be overwhelming for your relative. There are so many new faces and people, not to mention a new environment and routine. Arrange to stay for a meal with your relative or a cup of tea as you might at home. The administrator or manager may not be on duty at the weekend.

Afternoons are normally preferable to mornings for admissions. This may be discussed at the pre-assessment stage. It provides an opportunity for a senior member of staff to meet your relative before they move in. Relatives can liaise with staff at this stage to make sure important personal 'ritual' and routines are considered and tailor the transition process to their needs.

Establish relationships with the staff, particularly the manager and the key worker who takes responsibility for your relative. Discuss ways in which you might like to get involved in the life of the home, especially if you are likely to be a regular visitor. Help your relative build confidence in the new surroundings. Adjustment to moving in varies with different people. When a relative is confused or highly dependent, it is sometimes difficult to know how they will react. Reassure your relative by saying that you will be staying with them for a while. Some find it difficult to say 'goodbye' and develop other rituals for parting to prevent a difficult emotional reaction.

**Admission example from Cherry Tree Residential Home (for people with dementia)**

**2pm** – arrival with a quiet introduction and cup of tea with the family and manager. A welcome pack is given and the key worker is introduced.

Furniture will have been already placed in room, a couple of days beforehand, as pre-arranged with the home.

The resident and family are shown to the room and familiar objects and pieces are highlighted.

The family are then asked about preferences and routines, preferred name and so on.

The key worker helps the resident unpack their case and put clothes and items in selected areas.

An inventory of items in the room is made.

**4pm** – the resident and family are taken round the rest of the home and are offered tea in the communal lounge together before the family leaves.

Reassurance and introductions to other staff and residents.

Every 15 minutes the key worker comes back to reassure the resident.

**8pm** – the new resident is often very tired and is helped to bed.

2-hourly checks are carried out at night with additional visits (if triggered by a sensor mat which detects when someone gets out of bed).

# Helping someone to settle in

People take varied amounts of time to settle into a new environment. On average, it can take between six and twelve weeks. The process of settling in and fitting in needs to take whatever time it needs.

When a resident has been actively involved in the decision making, the period of adjustment is likely to be easier. Especially as moving into a care home is triggered more by necessity than desire. It is particularly important to preserve a private life within a community living context – living much of their lives in a public domain may take a bit of getting used to. A new social structure, friendships, norms of behaviour and different types of people can be quite a culture shock. Hopefully, the manager has briefed all the staff so they can make the experience easier. They can explain what happens at different times and introduce your relative to others who might befriend them or 'show them the ropes'. A good home will want to involve residents in helping your relative to settle in.

Leaving your relative alone at the home for the first time can be difficult, particularly for those with memory difficulties. Engage the support of a sensitive member of staff so that your relative does not feel abandoned. Ask them to give some emotional reassurance if your relative needs it after you leave.

### Suggestions to help your relative settle

- Think about the things which might help your relative during this time of change and uncertainty.
- Help them face the reality of the situation, their new environment and routines by being alongside them if you can. Explain things, affirm, remind and encourage your relative during the settling in period.
- Help your relative to keep their relationships active with friends and other members of the family and organisations of significance by helping with correspondence, emails and so on.
- Share the emotional aspects of the move to help them restore a sense of equilibrium.
- Help them to keep their sense of self and control. Personalise rooms, pass information on to staff about what is important and how they can best maintain a sense of competence and control in their lives *within their capabilities*.

- Help staff to understand the personal life story. This will help your relative use the past to help put the present into perspective.

- Suggest ideas about activities they might enjoy to the activity organiser/staff.

- Negotiate with staff tasks and roles, such as aspects of caring, that you and the resident want to maintain.

- Create a good relationship with staff. This will have a major influence on mutual understanding.

- Introduce your relative to fresh air and the outdoor environment and different aspects of the home early in their stay. Familiarise them early to build confidence in their surroundings.

## Keeping in touch

Although visits may be limited, there are other ways of keeping in touch. Letters, telephone calls or emails can all be appropriate. Encourage the people that matter to them to stay in contact to avoid them feeling cut off or abandoned. This can be done in various ways. One way might be to accompany older friends or grandchildren on their first visit to the care home early on. Help them share the experience and become familiar with the new setting. Some care homes are also linking into new technologies, such as Skype, which will make it easier for residents to maintain links with families who live further away.

## Visits

For those visiting from long distances, some homes will arrange for you to dine with your relative in privacy. For people visiting regularly, coming and going, making themselves a drink or joining your relative for coffee and tea will become second nature. Visits can be important 'emotional highlights' for your relative and it is important to know how to make the most of these.

These activities may help the visiting experience:

- care giving activities (helping with personal care, laundry, room layout and linking care to former lifestyle)
- creating a personalised environment
- and maintaining links with the former life
- pampering with favourite foods, activities and music
- comforting by sitting and talking to reduce anxiety
- engaging with favourite activities, photos and scrap books
- educating staff about your relative's key characteristics and helping them to understand behaviours
- monitoring their status and ensuring lifestyle and clothes are appropriate
- mediating in a range of decisions (such as meals, foot care and aspects of personalising care).

## When to visit

Conflicting advice is confusing. When should you visit and how often to help your relative settle as quickly as possible during this transition period? Your relative's desire to see you and other family and friends is a basic human right. Of course, much depends on your individual relationship and the practicalities of life. Some homes advise leaving a few days or a week to help your relative settle. But you are best placed to know your relative and what is most likely to help them. Remember there are other ways of keeping in touch.

## Family involvement

Most families remain involved in the lives of their relatives throughout their stay. They play key roles in negotiating, monitoring and mediating as advocates. Family visits can greatly improve quality of life. They help people to maintain their sense of identity while creating a sense of continuity and community. For those with severe dementia, it can be distressing not to be recognised by your relative or to feel unappreciated at other times. But maintaining interest through visits can help the staff help you to monitor your relative's general well-being.

Many families are unfamiliar with the culture of a care home. Each care home has its own routines and different ways of doing things – some may be unexpected. Most good homes will encourage family members to be involved and even enlist them as an important link to the outside world. For those who have difficulty actually getting to the home some provide names of other residents' relatives who might be prepared to share a car or taxi or who may offer over night accommodation.

## Dealing with challenging reactions

### Ways of helping a relative with dementia or other mental health conditions

Feelings of disorientation, fear, blame, accusation and angry outbursts or being uncooperative (towards you or the staff) can occur, particularly if your relative feels afraid or abandoned and has no sense of reassuring familiarity. This can result in varied responses, depending on the individual's stage of dementia and the circumstances around them at that particular moment. It is important to understand how best to respond to them in these difficult moments, although you cannot always get this right. One golden rule is to look at the feelings behind the behaviour and understand the underlying need. It is not always obvious, but very often, the reaction will be due to fear or anxiety. This may be linked to a loss, insecurity, or lack of role or purpose.

Often feelings are triggered by an unmet need. This may be due to something from the past as well as from the present in the jumble of memories. Whatever the level of cognitive impairment, maintain integrity. Manipulating or misleading your relative may break trust and make the situation worse. By addressing the underlying feelings, your relative is likely to feel their needs are at least acknowledged. There is usually a good reason behind the behaviour of older disorientated people. Although we cannot always know why a person behaves in a certain way, we can help them to express emotions and accompany them during these stressful moments.

95

# Emotional effects

After moving your relative, it is normal to feel some guilt or a sense of having let them down in some way, even if it is the best possible solution and one which may allow positive changes in them as they settle in. Finding other like-minded relatives can help a lot – some homes offer much appreciated emotional support for relatives. This contributes to positive trusting relationships. Staff can offer reassurance by telling you how your relative has fared since the last visit. Sometimes changes or deterioration can make visiting more stressful. It is important to ask how best to manage the situation and understand the reasons.

Some families describe their role as 'care watcher'. Even if you are a close relative, you could be out of touch with their changed capabilities and this could lead to unrealistic expectations. Sometimes negative feelings, often associated with loss, can lead to criticisms of staff, overprotectiveness or confrontation. It can be an attempt to prove to yourself and others that you care. Genuine concerns should be raised with the appropriate individual. A good home will listen carefully and help relatives to understand the problem, as discussed in **Step Nine**.

It can be upsetting if staff don't appear to understand how you might be feeling. You may still want to contribute or they may overlook your expertise. Communicate with them and help them understand your perspective. Mutual understanding goes a long way to smoothing over potential problems.

Karen found it difficult to hand over her responsibility for her mother Jean. She had looked after her for seven years after she was diagnosed with dementia. There was clearly no right or wrong way to cope with this situation and she relied on her instincts. No one prepared her about how she might feel (the bewilderment, sadness and resentment) or helped her to move on and let go. Walking away from her mother on her first day was a feeling she could never forget. But, in time, she slowly built trust with the 'new' carers. This helped her to 'let go' and start living again. Karen says, 'It was helpful to find some other like-minded relatives who joined with me in the local pub for a drink. We formed the beginnings of our relatives' group'.

## Advice lines

A listening ear over the phone (from organisations such as the Relatives & Residents Association) can be invaluable. You can raise any concerns from you or your relative. The helpline also provides a listening service and allows ample time for callers to share their stories and express their feelings. There may be no one else to share these with. You may feel angry, tearful or guilty about the decision made, inadequate or disappointed. An understanding and experienced ear of a 'knowledgeable friend' can do a lot to help and guide. People call with funding queries, questions about care plans, quality of life and issues arising from hospital discharge as well as personal worries. This type of independent service can be enormously reassuring.

## Finding a new role for yourself

### Linking to the outside world

Remember, you still have a vital role as a point of contact between the community, the staff and your relative. It may take time to establish your role, and that of family and friends, but staff will recognise its importance and help your relative maintain these links.

# Summary

## Step Six • Moving in

- After admission make sure you and your relative have:
  - a copy of the contract with the home
  - the handbook
  - information about any illness your relative has
  - involvement in personalising the room, considering useful items, memorabilia and leisure enjoyment
  - involvement in the initial care planning (where your relative wishes this).

- If your relative has dementia, give the home:
  - a list of key dates and people of significance to your relative
  - if you were the carer, some idea about the caring relationship
  - information about cultural and religious beliefs
  - habits and personal routines.

- Make sure you have access to legal and financial advice and understand all aspects of the contract before you sign it.

- You have an important role in helping your relative settle in and preserving their links with the outside world.

# Step Seven
## Learning the ropes

You have probably seen
many care homes from
the outside. But until this
phase of your life, there
may have been no reason to
find out what goes on inside.
This chapter will help
you understand how
care homes work – who
does what, the services
that are provided, typical
routines and activities
that happen day-to-day
and some of the rules and
regulations that govern how
homes are run.

# How a care home is run

## Staff and structure – who's who?

As described in **Step Two**, there are different ways in which homes are owned and managed. A small number are run by social services departments or NHS trusts. Most are now in what is called the 'independent sector' and either run for 'profit' or 'not for profit'. Some are owned and run by charities with boards of trustees, others as private businesses. Many homes are owned singly by a proprietor. Others are part of a small group of two or three privately owned places. Medium-sized groups of homes may cover a geographical area or cater for a special group. And there are increasingly large groups of homes with well-known brands and some with the backing of financial organisations.

The owner or senior manager of the home usually employs a manager to take care of operational details within their management and leadership role. This person has to be registered as the responsible person by the Inspectorate (to be called the Care Quality Commission as of April 2009). A registered nurse will be in charge of care in a nursing home.

### Administrator

The first person with whom you are likely to have contact if you visit or telephone is the home's administrator. This person does not get involved in hands-on care for residents but supports the manager in dealing with enquiries, keeping records up-to-date, handling residents' finances and so on. They can tell you about the resident's personal allowance, give you a statement and take a message for the manager or a member of staff. They will not be able to answer health- or care-related questions.

### Senior staff

Most larger homes have a tier of senior staff below the manager. They have responsibility for day-to-day running of aspects of the home. They will often be responsible for part of the home (for example, one unit or floor, or the nursing unit where registered nurses will be in charge). They ensure care plans are in place and are regularly updated. They supervise care staff so they provide the right care for residents. If you have a query about your relative's care or would like an update on how they are getting on, speak first with the person in charge of the unit they live in, rather than the manager.

They will have much more information and will know your relative better. In the senior team, as well as 'unit managers' or 'team leaders' who head up care activities, there may also be other heads of departments (for example, in charge of cleaning, laundry, catering, activities and maintenance).

### Care staff/key workers

Care staff deliver hands on support for residents. They help with 'activities of daily living' (such as getting up and dressed in the morning, washing, bathing, eating, drinking, toileting and helping residents by providing a magazine or paper to look at or helping them attend a social activity). They may be called 'care assistants', 'support workers' or 'carers'. Some may be experienced care workers and have a more senior post, perhaps a title like 'senior carer'. Some homes have 'key worker' systems, with members of the care team allocated to individual residents for whom they have special responsibility. The job of the key worker varies from home to home. It might just mean checking they have enough toiletries or be much more detailed (including writing a life history and linking closely with friends and family members). It usually entails putting the care plan into practice. In a nursing home, the care assistant will have designated responsibilities under a 'named nurse' or nurse in charge.

### Activities staff

Activities staff are responsible for assessing the social and occupational needs of residents and providing activities to suit their needs and interests. The 'activity co-ordinator' or 'organiser' might be a full- or part-time post. The hours depend on the size of the home and the needs of residents. However, there are no rules laid down (as there might be for nursing ratios) so this tends to be influenced by resources and the management's emphasis on this aspect of provision, so will vary between homes. As a rule, the staff time allocated to activity is dependent on the size of the home. It might be the responsibility of one person, shared between staff visiting on a sessional basis and in-house staff, or a combination of these. The trend is to have a person co-ordinating and managing activities. Their job is to provide a range of activity suited to the needs and abilities of residents, involving different people for aspects of the activity provision depending on which activities are included in the care plans.

Some activities may be planned in advance for a programme. Others happen informally during the day and are therefore not always set out in a programme. Regular planned activities might include painting, gentle exercise, aromatherapy massage, musical activities, quizzes, bingo, baking or film showings. These are arranged following consultation with residents. Activities might well include volunteers, local community organisations, relatives and outside specialists (in creative activities, exercise, or entertainment) who are brought in. Outings and fundraising events may also feature in the calendar.

Some activities organisers also have care roles. Though this can create a conflict if the home is short staffed for whatever reason. Providing activities for people with dementia is a skilled role requiring specialist training. There is more spontaneity in activity provision for people with dementia. Staff tend to 'go with the flow' responding to moods and inclinations of residents. There are standards for activity provision available from www.cot.org.uk (the College of Occupational Therapist's website).

### Domestic staff

Domestic staff are employed to clean the home, launder clothing and linen, ensure the building and garden are well maintained and work in the kitchen. They often make close relationships with residents. It is helpful if they have good interpersonal skills and can engage residents in conversation while they are cleaning their room, for example.

> Martin was surprised but pleased to find out that his dad, Arthur, had become friendly with the home's maintenance man, John. They had discovered that they were both railway enthusiasts when John had noticed a picture on Arthur's wall. John made a habit of popping in on Arthur. He recognised that, with few men in the home, a bit of male company was appreciated. They chatted about their experiences on the railways and Arthur began to accompany John in some of his tasks, even helping out where he could. Martin noticed Arthur's mood had improved and he seemed more settled in the home.

# The manager's role and influence

Just as in other organisations, the contribution of the manager is vital in shaping the environment and ethos of a care home and providing strong and positive leadership.

It is a demanding role, requiring many different qualities and abilities, particularly good communication skills. If the home provides nursing care, the manager may be a registered nurse. All managers must have a management qualification equivalent of NVQ Level 4.

Managers should have an overall knowledge of what is happening in the home, but may delegate specific roles to members of the team (such as responsibility for training). Ultimately, though, managers are responsible for all the day-to-day decisions affecting the home:

- residents can only be admitted with the manager's agreement and many are actively involved in assessing prospective residents
- managers are responsible for recruiting, training and managing all staff, though they will often employ senior staff to support them in this
- they organise rotas
- managers must put in place and monitor all the necessary systems to ensure the health, safety and well-being of staff, residents and visitors
- managers must be conversant with the legislation and guidelines relating to care homes, ensuring they are fully met
- managers have to maintain links with external agencies (such as the inspection service, social services departments and GP practices), local community organisations (such as churches) and relatives and friends of residents
- managers set the tone and culture of a home
- managers need financial and business acumen as they are responsible for ensuring the home is profitable and has sound financial systems and a business plan for future development
- managers are responsible for quality improvement in the home and linking this to learning and practice development.

## Care plans and risk assessments

Your relative's care plan is a key document because it contains guidance which will inform quality of life and the care they receive. Homes have their own systems for recording personal information, some are paper-based, whereas others have introduced computerised record-keeping.

Some care plan approaches start with what the person can still do (they are 'strengths-based') and others focus on areas of need. Some keep records in a central place (such as the nurses' office) whereas others also have a copy of the plan in the residents' rooms. In **Step Six** we discussed the areas of information you will need to give staff as early as possible. The care plan contains information on holistic needs, enabling staff to look after the 'whole person'.

## Support needs

The care plan should be detailed with descriptions of tasks which need support, diagnosed medical conditions, treatment that has been prescribed and how it is to be given, and relevant details about your relative's diet and preferred lifestyle (when they like to get up and go to bed and so on). As well as stating specific care needs, the care plan should paint a picture of the person, describing their personality and summarising their life story. As well as physical and medical needs, it should cover social, occupational, spiritual and emotional needs.

## Managing risk

We all live with a degree of risk that is why your resident's care plan may have areas of risk assessment. These detail any potential dangers and negotiate how they will be managed, rather than avoiding risk altogether. The kind of areas where risk may be involved include:

- a resident smoking
- a resident being prone to falls
- a resident with a history of weight loss
- a resident being likely to get lost were they to leave the building.

## Contributing to the care plan

The care plan is a document which the resident and agreed family members contribute to. It should be given to your relative or you to check and sign. This is required under the Care Standards Act. If your relative is happy for you to see their care plan, you can ask to look at it at any time. Bear in mind, however, that care plans contain private information so staff have a duty to maintain the confidentiality of your relative. If the plan is stored on a computer, it is also governed by the Data Protection Act.

A care plan is a living document, which is constantly updated. Daily notes are added by staff, summarising how the resident has been. Ever-changing needs mean that the care plan needs reviewing on a regular basis. The frequency of reviews will vary from home to home and they are often updated as needs dictate. Regularly (possibly every six months or when needs change) there will be a review meeting in which relatives and key staff take part, as well as other involved people (for example, a social services care manager).

It was a great help to Mavis that staff had several discussions with her about her husband, William's, care plan when he moved into the home and she was grateful that they took on board her ideas for looking after William. But they hit an obstacle when it came to the subject of William going out in the garden for a walk. Staff had noticed how much William enjoyed being outside and Mavis explained it was because he had been a keen gardener. The sticking point was that Mavis was reluctant for William to go in the garden unless someone was with him all the time in case he had a fall. His Parkinson's made him unsteady on his feet. She wanted the patio door from his room to be kept locked. Staff gently urged Mavis to see the situation from William's point of view, saying that they did not want him to feel locked up. They pointed out that we all take risks as part of our everyday lives. Mavis eventually came round to their way of thinking. In time, she had to admit that the freedom to go in the garden made William calmer and happier.

## Medical care and visiting professionals

Older people living in care homes have the same right to use the range of health services available to any person living in the community, though it can sometimes be difficult to access specific help. Some services visit the home rather than asking the resident to go to a surgery or clinic.

## GPs

Homes tend to have a contract with a local GP surgery which looks after most of their residents, though, as we said earlier in the book, older people are entitled to keep their GP. In larger homes especially, the GP may visit at set times each week so you can arrange to speak with them. In between regular visits, staff can of course call out the GP. If a doctor looks after only a handful of residents, it is likely that visits will be as need arises.

Residents' medication is obtained through their GP, as are medical support services and referrals to specialists. Many conditions of later life are progressive so it is vital that their health needs are assessed on a regular basis. Staff can request a thorough health check from every resident's GP at least once a year. This is their right to identify any new needs, screen for common complaints in later life and review medication.

## Visiting nurses

Homes providing nursing care have their own round the clock nurses. But homes providing personal care rely on district nurses and nurses attached to GP practices. Like GPs, district nurses often have a regular slot when they visit to attend to needs such as wound dressing. There may also be specialist nurses (such as palliative care specialists, continence advisors and community psychiatric nurses) who give training and advice and look after particular residents.

## Physiotherapists, chiropodists, occupational therapists and speech and language therapists

If the home has an intermediate care or rehabilitation unit, it may employ its own physiotherapists but most homes rely on community physiotherapists. Chiropody can be difficult to access via the NHS and some families supplement the NHS service by using a private chiropodist. Staff are limited in what they can do with residents' feet (particularly those who are diabetic). Foot care is essential to keep older people comfortable, pain-free and mobile.

Occupational therapists (OTs), as described in earlier chapters, advise on ensuring that the environment is safe and accessible and they provide guidance on a range of 'quality of life' issues. They keep people active. Some occupational therapists are employed by the NHS and others are in private practice. Speech and language therapists also help care home staff support residents in communication and with swallowing difficulties. They may help residents who have had a stroke regain speech and may offer suggestions for enhancing the communication of people with dementia. Many people (who have suffered strokes or have dementia, in particular) have difficulty eating and swallowing. Speech and language therapists assess individuals and advise on the consistency of food needed as well as equipment for eating safely and independently.

## Why homes may decide a person is inappropriately placed

Regular monitoring of your relative's needs may show these can no longer be met in the home. If it is a home providing only personal care, there may come a time when a nursing home is needed. There might be occasions when the behaviour of a person with dementia makes it difficult for them to stay, or where relationships with other residents have become strained (perhaps due to personality clashes). If the resident is funded by social services, the care manager will be asked to review their needs. If homes keep residents they are not able to care for, they are in breach of their registration. But there are situations where homes can keep a person by putting in more staff, for example. If there is a possibility a resident may need to be placed in another home because of changing needs, you should be informed early on so they have time to plan. You should not be given short notice to quit.

## The role of acute hospitals

Residents in care homes use hospitals in much the same way as older people living in their own homes. Where full assessment is not possible at the home (if, for example, a scan is needed), the resident would visit as a day case. You might be asked to accompany them on outpatient visits.

## Staff training

### Induction training

Newly recruited care staff cannot work with residents until the home has received their Criminal Records Bureau (CRB) check and they have been given induction training. Induction training (laid down by a set of national Common Induction Standards) contains core topics:

- understanding the principles of care
- understanding the organisation and the role of the worker
- maintaining safety at work
- communicating effectively
- recognising and responding to abuse and neglect
- some homes have additional topics included such as understanding culture and the importance of activities, communication and person-centred care.

**Mandatory**

There are several areas of what are called 'mandatory' training. Even well-established staff must have annual refreshers. These are:

- moving and handling
- POVA (protection of vulnerable adults)
- health and safety
- fire safety
- emergency first aid.

Fire safety training must be provided twice a year, the other topics annually.

**Specialist training**

The home will also need to show it gives training relevant to the client group being cared for. So if it is a dementia care home, all staff will need training on dementia. Recent studies by organisations like the Alzheimer's Society have argued that, since two-thirds of older people in care homes have dementia, training on dementia care should be more widely available. Several organisations have training programmes through which staff can be accredited in dementia care.

# Qualifications

The government has set standards for training in care homes. At least 50% of staff should have an NVQ (National Vocational Qualification) Level 2. Some care homes have a much higher proportion of their staff trained to this level and may also have staff at Levels 3 and 4. NVQs vary in content and are not specialist. The focus is on assessing knowledge rather than providing training. Registered nurses in a care home have to demonstrate they are updating their skills and knowledge to stay on the NMC (Nursing and Midwifery Council) register and practise as a nurse in this country. They are responsible for developing a learning culture in the home such as coaching and mentoring staff on the job.

# Organising and delivering training

As the person who is responsible for quality improvement within the home, the manager has overall responsibility for training. Some managers select staff to attend particular courses, which ensures the staff develop the skills where needed. Others allow them to opt in to ones that catch their interest. Some pay staff their normal rate while in training, and this is good practice. Others expect them to attend in their own time. Again, some homes simply take staff off the floors when a training session is going on, others bring them in on a day they would not normally be working.

There are often members of staff in a home, besides the manager, with responsibility for aspects of training. Some homes have parts of their training available for staff to complete on-line, others have workbooks and training packs. Freelance trainers may deliver training on a specific topic, such as sensory loss. The local NHS may have training on health-related aspects of caring, such as continence care. Social services may arrange training and offer a proportion of places to care homes. It does not happen often but, when relatives and residents are both involved in training, staff can hear about their experiences and ideas can be shared. Some areas of staff training are potentially very useful for you, too. For instance, training on helping a person with eating might be valuable if you help at mealtimes.

## Access to information in the home

The home should have resources available for staff (and hopefully relatives) to help them keep up-to-date with the latest ideas in the field of care. There may be factsheets from the larger charities supporting older people, magazines on relevant topics (such as the *Journal of Dementia Care* or *My Home Life Bulletins*) and a selection of books and DVDs.

## Rules and regulations

Care homes have to comply with a whole range of legislation. This means care home managers have to be familiar with the law as it affects the care of older people. The most important piece of legislation affecting care homes is the Care Standards Act. This lays down regulations for how homes are to operate. Homes are also bound by laws in employing staff. This includes the need for Criminal Records Bureau checks on new staff, since they will be working with vulnerable adults. Another aspect of the rules homes must abide by are the staffing levels set down through the registration and inspection process. These vary depending on the people being looked after and their levels of need. Some of the legal framework which influences what happens in homes is related to health and safety.

A new law which will have implications for care homes is the Mental Capacity Act 2005 (described in **Step Three**). At the moment, the Human Rights Act applies just to services that are publicly provided but there have been efforts to extend it to private organisations. An example of the areas covered by the Human Rights Act is the right to 'a private and family life'.

## Standards and Inspections

The Care Standards Act 2000 and the Care Homes Regulations 2001 meant that, for the first time, care homes across the country had the same standards to meet. The 38 national standards for homes are set at a minimum level, so of course can be exceeded by homes. These are about to change to a system of outcome standards yet to be defined. There are 46 regulations which have the statutes of law. As mentioned in other chapters, when they are visiting homes, inspectors also have eight main areas they are looking at called KLORA (Key Lines of Regulatory Assessment). The Standards are being reviewed at the moment so there may be changes over the coming years.

Care homes want to do well in their inspections. Not only because the inspectors ultimately have the power to shut them down if they are failing but also because more and more families read their reports to help them decide on a home. All inspections are now unannounced so the manager has no prior warning. If it is a key inspection, it may last several hours. The inspector(s) will spend time speaking with members of staff, residents and any visitors who are in the home, as well as looking at documentation. If it is a home for people with dementia, they may also spend time in structured observation to measure well-being in the residents.

On the day, they give verbal feedback. A few weeks later, the home receives a draft report which it can challenge. The final report states how the home is performing in particular categories with four possible levels. These are 'weighted'. Sometimes homes feel the results are misleading in some areas. If the rating is good, the next key inspection may not be for over two years. In the meantime, the manager must submit annual information on the service and their plans for improving it (including what residents and relatives have said about the quality of what is provided). The inspector makes both requirements and recommendations. Inspection requirements are where standards are not met so changes must be made. Recommendations made following an inspection are suggestions for improvements.

The home may also be monitored by organisations which have beds (such as the local social services or Primary Care Trust) who check if the contract the home has with the authority is being met. Fees being paid may depend on how well the home is meeting the contract. A third source of monitoring for care homes is checks made by the company which owns the home.

They are required under the Care Standards Act to make regular visits to ensure the service is up to standard. They have to send their report to the Inspectorate.

# Daily life in a care home

## Routines and experiences of residents

Gone are the days when it was acceptable to run a care home for the convenience of staff. The emphasis is now on older people carrying on with the way of life they had when they were living in their own homes. Though there is often flexibility over when breakfast is taken, lunch-time and evening meals tend to be at fixed points. Staff are also likely to have set times for helping residents take prescribed medications. There may be a timetable with some activities, too. This provides a bit of structure and routine over the course of the week. Other fixed points are shift patterns for staff. Handover sessions scheduled between shifts allow new staff coming on duty to be updated.

Residents are free to spend their time where they choose. Though staff might discourage them from spending all their time in their room, ultimately it is your relative's own choice. Some people feel most comfortable in their room surrounded by reminders of their earlier life, their own choice of music and books. It is important to recognise and support this choice. Most residents divide their time between their rooms and the communal spaces. Sometimes they have to compromise between themselves over how to use shared spaces but access to them should not be restricted. A shared area that can be harder to access is the garden, particularly if the doors are kept locked.

Elizabeth anticipated that when her mum, Ivy, was in the home, she would benefit from the company of the other residents and from joining in with activities. She was disappointed to find her mum spent most days in her room and asked staff what they had done to encourage her to be part of the group. Staff told her that they invited Ivy to take part in the sessions run by the activities organiser but that Ivy had said 'No'. All they could do was keep suggesting it but it was Ivy's choice and they could not force her to do anything. They reassured Elizabeth that it might take a while for her mum to feel confident in group activities but that most people start to socialise with other residents when they have had a little while to get used to the new environment.

## Services provided by care homes

### Support in personal care tasks

The most obvious form of help given by staff to residents in care homes is support in looking after themselves, for example, washing, dressing, going to the toilet and shaving. The aim is to support people in doing as much as possible for themselves within their capabilities. Sometimes older people in care homes expect staff to do everything for them. Time pressures can even make it easier for staff to do this. But this reduces their independence and may undermine dignity and the individual's sense of being in control of their life.

### Meals

All meals and drinks are provided in 24 hour care. The home will have its own daily routines of meals and snacks, but if people want a snack in between meals, staff can usually supply this. In some homes, chefs are employed to plan and cook meals. In other homes, meals are ordered and delivered. Delivered meals may be chilled or frozen with special equipment available to reheat them safely. They can be a good option as they are prepared under strict hygiene conditions and with careful attention to nutrition. Visitors can usually be catered for, though advance notice is helpful.

### Comfortable, well-maintained, safe and accessible environment

The home is also responsible for providing a place to live which is pleasant and easy to get around. It should have all the necessary disability aids and equipment. And it should be kept clean, warm and smelling pleasant. To ensure this, homes employ domestic staff to clean and maintenance staff to look after the building and grounds.

### Laundry service

Homes have to look after their residents' clothes and bedding, usually employing laundry staff to take care of these tasks. Sometimes, staff also take on the job of carrying out repairs to clothing. The laundry will probably be out of bounds to visitors but you might be shown it when you are looking round the home. Most homes use commercial washing machines and tumble dryers to cope with the heavy demands placed on them.

## Friendship and relationships

One of the great benefits of moving into a care home is the opportunity for social contact. As people settle in, they forge friendships with other residents and staff – some people say it is like having a whole new family. It is understandable for new residents to be timid in the early days, but in time, many find their feet socially.

## Opportunities to engage in meaningful activity

Another benefit of being in a home is that there can be a lot to do and stimulate interest (depending on the home). One of the areas on which homes are inspected is the extent to which they provide meaningful things to occupy residents. This includes group and individual activities, outings and entertainment. Staff should find out about each resident's interests, encourage them to continue with hobbies and pastimes or even try new things.

If they have been used to going about in the local neighbourhood and have belonged to a church, club or society, there is no reason for their involvement to stop. Staff may need to discuss the best ways of supporting a person in maintaining these practices and links with friends and family.

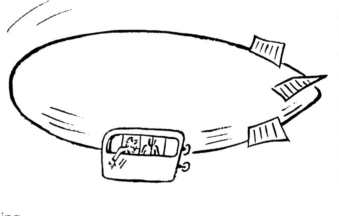

## Extra services which may incur cost

Although full board and 24 hour care (and, in some homes, nursing) are covered in the fees for homes, there are extras with are charged additionally. The home may arrange for a hairdresser or chiropodist to visit, for instance. But if the resident chooses to use these services, they will have to pay for them out of their allowance.

## Spiritual support

Meeting the needs of the 'whole person' includes attending to their spiritual needs. Homes often do this by having regular services run by local churches, hosting visiting ministers or arranging for residents to be accompanied to their own places of worship. An increasing number of homes are now setting aside a 'quiet room' or 'multi-faith room' which can be used by residents, staff and visitors for prayer and reflection. Staff may be willing to read prayers and should also support residents in practising their beliefs (including fasting, rituals around purification and praying).

# The pattern of a 'normal day'

A 'typical day' can be a mystery to relatives and friends. If family members visit at a 'quiet' time of day, it can feel as if not much happens at all. Looking at photographs or hearing reports from staff can be reassuring.

Each day should include something which is different as it is 'variety' which gives 'spice to life'. Quite a bit of time is taken up with the caring aspects of the work that staff do (helping people get up and dressed and looking after their daily needs). These tasks can be quite time-consuming for people with limited stamina and independence, particularly if staff are encouraging them to do as much as possible for themselves. But a mundane activity like getting dressed or having a bath can become an enjoyable experience and an opportunity to talk. Mealtimes and snacks also take up a significant proportion of daily time. These too should be unhurried, social occasions, a highlight of the person's day, with time given to eat comfortably with the right level of help. The rest of the day is divided between resting and relaxing, taking part in activities the home provides and spending time with visitors according to the wishes of the individual.

## Hygiene

Because of the age and frailty of the people they are looking after, staff in care homes have to pay careful attention to hygiene in order to avoid the spread of infection. Many homes have alcohol hand cleaning dispensers at various points. Visitors are encouraged to use these when arriving and leaving. The gels are not a substitute for hand-washing, though, and ideally should be used after hands have been washed thoroughly.

Just like a restaurant, the home's kitchen will be regularly inspected for health and hygiene purposes by the local authority. There is restricted access to the main kitchen to keep the environment clean. Those allowed in wear protective clothing.

Because of continence problems, it is hard to avoid odours altogether. But the vigilance of care staff and frequent carpet-shampooing can keep them to a minimum. Homes have rooms for disposing of human waste hygienically, called 'sluice rooms'. They will also have robust laundry practices to make sure germs are killed (for example, bedding and clothing are washed at high temperatures).

Standard domestic fabrics and floor coverings are not designed for the use received in care homes. Homes are furnished with materials that are easy to clean, hardwearing and hygienic. Floors, chairs and wheelchairs need washing constantly. Sometimes cleaning furniture falls to domestic staff, sometimes maintenance staff. Night staff can also be given particular tasks.

## Quality of life and activities

It is difficult to measure the quality of another person's life. We are not them and it is hard to imagine what makes for a fulfilling existence at their age and stage of life. Many relatives see a close link between quality of life and the type and range of activities available in a home. Activities are mainly about offering residents variety and enjoyment. They can help prevent boredom and provide a social focus. Another purpose is to keep the older person active by engaging them in doing things they find stimulating. Activities can maintain health, fitness and agility. They can bolster confidence and protect residents from common mental health problems like depression.

Each person has their own interests and residents vary in their ability to do different activities. Some are limited by cognitive decline, others by physical frailty. Their needs and abilities will change over time and so need to be revisited on a regular basis. Group activities can be adapted so that people can join in at whatever level is suitable, though. They can also be about an individual following their hobby or meaningful experience within their capabilities (see **Appendix 4**) with support from staff. This is especially true for frailer residents, nearing the end of their lives, and those in the more advanced stages of dementia.

Some homes have a monthly or yearly budget from which staff can buy equipment or pay for events and entertainment. In other homes, fundraising takes place to cover these costs. This might be a raffle at Christmas or a summer fete. Homes will often have resources (games, books, jigsaws and so on) available in the lounges of each unit so staff can initiate activities. Friends and relatives can also use them when visiting. There are specialist suppliers of equipment but it can be cheaper for homes to buy items on sale in general shops. Donations from visitors, particularly of reminiscence items, are greatly appreciated, as is help with fundraising and offering time as a volunteer.

Most homes organise trips through the year, though going out in the warmer months is better for people who are frail. Because older people enter homes when they are more frail than they used to be, ambitious outings involving long journeys are becoming less appropriate, though they may still suit some. Visiting a local attraction, having lunch at a pub or garden centre, or going to the theatre or a local shopping centre are some popular outings. Arranging transport suitable for people with mobility problems can be difficult and expensive. Booking a coach can be a high risk strategy if residents are likely to change their mind about going on the day. Taking a small group somewhere nearby in a taxi or minibus is easier and cheaper to arrange and can feel more 'normal'.

Look for information about activities and outings on the home's notice board. Details will usually be displayed prominently in the foyer of the home. The home may also have a newsletter which lists dates of planned events. Talk to the activities or admin staff for more information.

## Relationships

When people go into care homes, the pattern of their relationships changes. While studies show that relationships with relatives and friends are still their top priority, they make new bonds. Having to depend on them for support, your relative may become close to staff. This means staff have earned their trust. Your own relationship will settle into a new pattern. Visiting in a home is different from spending time with your relative at home. They may, at times, be angry and blame you. It can be difficult to know what to talk about. Other relationships may also go through a difficult patch. Some friends and family members might never overcome the awkwardness and, ultimately, stop visiting.

The other residents in the home are people with whom your relative now spends a lot of time. They may make close friendships with some. There may be others they don't get on with. This is a normal part of living together. You might find them reserved in relationships with other residents, keeping them at arm's length. This may be their way of maintaining some privacy and personal space.

## Nutrition

Food is such an important part of life in a care home it warrants its own section. Your relative should have food they can eat easily and enjoy and which meets their nutritional needs. You can play an important part in ensuring this happens through your knowledge of their tastes and habits. Menus are often displayed in the entrance and dining areas of a home. There may be a cycle of menus so that there is variety over the course of a month. Most homes offer choices with residents deciding, perhaps the day before or for people with dementia, on the day, what they will have as well as being able to influence what is on the menu. Meals play an important part of life in a care home. Menus should reflect the seasons and have plenty of fresh fruit and vegetables. Homes also cater for special diets. They provide not just diabetic and gluten free diets but ethnic dishes for those from other cultures to observe food laws (for example, Halal and kosher food).

People's needs, tastes and appetites change as they get older. The senses of smell and taste can become poor, so people like highly flavoured food. Someone who never liked curries may now enjoy them. Sometimes people develop cravings for sweet foods. Smaller portions are preferred and it can be off-putting to be overfaced with a large plate of food you know you cannot manage. Older people are also at a higher risk of being undernourished than the general population so having a balanced diet is essential for health in many ways. It helps with wound healing and maintains healthy bones to name just two. Similarly, dehydration can have many unfortunate consequences for an older person's health. Yet many reduce what they drink if their mobility is limited, mistakenly believing they will not need to go to the toilet as often and be less at risk of an accident.

Ways of helping your relative eat well might include visiting at meals either to help them eat or share a meal with them. People eat better if meals are social occasions. Bring in nutritious treats you know they enjoy. If you take fruit or chocolate, or food you have cooked at home, let staff know as they need to be aware of what your relative has eaten.

Common difficulties with eating might need to be addressed at some point. For example, it is important to attend to dental health. Make sure that your relative's teeth and gums are checked regularly and that any dentures fit correctly and are not causing discomfort. Addressing dental problems is not always easy with people with dementia if you are not able to explain what is happening. Difficulties with chewing and swallowing can be caused by things like strokes and dementia. With the right approach and equipment, and food of the correct consistency, the risk of choking can be reduced. Older people in care homes can sometimes miss out on the expertise of dieticians, dentists and speech and language therapists so ask about the home's contact with these professionals, particularly if you are concerned your relative is not eating or drinking enough of the right things. You can also ask staff to keep a diary of what your relative eats and drinks if you are worried.

> Joyce was worried that Harold was not eating properly. It was understandable, given the bewilderment he must be feeling in his new setting. Staff in the care home gently encouraged Joyce to feel free to visit at mealtimes. If she would like to help her husband eat, that would be fine. She started a new routine, arriving late morning and staying over lunch to make sure Harold ate well. Staff said his appetite seemed better when Joyce was there. He was used to having her help and support at mealtimes. It was good for Joyce to continue with this aspect of Harold's care. She felt it was helping the staff to lessen their workload and she got to know them better. They seemed to like having her round at lunchtime and said it made the atmosphere more sociable and friendly.

## Dementia care

Details of how homes operate given above in this chapter relate to all homes (including homes looking after people with dementia) but there are several ways in which dementia care settings differ:

- the mix of staff will be different – staffing levels differ and staff have training in dementia care
- the buildings, décor and design of dementia care homes will be different
- you would expect to see different activities happening in a dementia care setting. Activities stimulating the senses would especially be in evidence.

# Safety and security

Care homes have a duty to keep their residents safe. If the building is not secure, there is a risk – not only of the wrong people getting in, but also of residents with dementia going out onto the street. Often, entry is by key code. Staff may not be supposed to give the code to certain visitors depending on their policy on security. There may also be coded doors within the building. Where homes have staff on reception during weekdays, it is relatively easy to get in but evenings and weekends can be frustrating. You will be asked to sign in the visitors' book stating the time you arrived and who you are visiting. When you leave you will sign out. This is necessary in case there is an emergency, such as a fire, as it will allow the emergency services to account for people who are in the building.

Residents can keep the key to their room unless they are assessed as being at risk in this situation. Some residents like the door locked when they are not in their room. Some lock the door when they are in the room to stop people coming in and out. Even where residents have a key to their room, staff have a master key. Homes may also provide a lockable drawer in every resident's room. This is not the best place to keep large quantities or money or expensive jewellery but is good for storing objects of sentimental value (such as letters or photographs). An inventory of a resident's property, regularly updated with new items brought in, helps keep track of belongings.

It can be frustrating, especially on a hot day, if windows in a care home cannot be opened to their full extent but they are kept on a latch for reasons of safety and security. Access to the garden may be restricted for similar reasons. Even if your relative is safe in the garden, other residents may be at risk of falling and need supervision while outdoors. The garden might not be fully secure either. There is a danger that a person with dementia could climb over a fence unseen by staff.

# Summary

## Step Seven • Learning the ropes

- Staff are employed in care homes with different responsibilities. Some provide hands-on care while others work in the kitchen, laundry or office. Training is required for these roles.

- The manager's role is a key appointment as they oversee everything that happens and can set the tone of the home.

- The care plan is a key document setting out how each resident will be supported in their daily lives. Relatives should be involved in creating the care plan and it should be reviewed and updated regularly.

- Homes have to operate to nationally agreed standards. Their success in meeting these standards is measured through regular inspections by the Commission for Social Care Inspection.

- As well as meeting basic care needs, homes provide stimulation and activity to give residents variety and quality of life.

- Moving into a care home brings new relationships and changes to existing relationships.

# Step Eight
# Getting involved

When someone close to you moves in to a care home it can feel like you are 'losing' them. Of course it may be a relief to be sharing the practical tasks of caring but it's important to remember that you still have a unique place in their life that is irreplaceable.

You shouldn't feel you are being shut out – be confident about getting involved with their new home. At the same time though, try not to feel under pressure to match up to what you think other people's expectations are – it's for you to discover the role you feel comfortable with.

## Care planning – what to expect

Care plans have been mentioned at various points in the book. Involving you is not an optional extra, it is something homes are required to do. The only valid reason a home could give for not involving you is if your relative has specifically asked them not to share the information with you. You are likely to be the expert when it comes to your relative. Staff may ask you to set aside time on the day of admission, or arrange a mutually convenient time close to this date. It will take time to put a detailed care plan in place, so don't worry if you later remember things you should have mentioned. Needs change, so care plans are reviewed on a regular basis. Ask to look at the care plan from time to time to check it is accurate. Request any changes necessary to reflect current needs.

**Step Six** looked at areas of the care plan to which you can contribute right from the start, particularly emphasising your role in providing biographical information. This is a reminder of the main areas to which you can contribute:

- health and care needs
- likes and dislikes, personality and lifestyle
- life history
- spiritual and cultural needs
- sexuality.

Kelly was nervous the first time she went to visit her nan, Ruby, the day after her move to the home. Where would her nan be? Should she speak to the staff? Were there rules about when you could visit and where you could go? She was relieved when she was met at the door by Maria, who introduced herself as Ruby's key worker. Maria explained that her nan's friend, Walter, had not stayed long the day before when he brought Ruby in. Could Kelly spend a few minutes telling Maria about Ruby's life as it would really help the staff who would be caring for her? It would give them things to talk about when they were with her. Ruby had had a severe stroke and was only slowly regaining her speech. Kelly was glad to be able to describe Ruby's life to Maria, how she had grown up in a terrace house the other side of town and been a dressmaker. She told Maria that Ruby's favourite night out was going to bingo every Wednesday. Kelly explained that when she had fallen out with her mum's boyfriend, she had gone to live with Ruby. They had always been close, and her nan was the person Kelly could talk to.

## Building relationships with staff

Alongside getting involved in your resident's care plan, your other key task at this point is building relationships with the staff in the home. If you invest some time and energy in establishing relationships, it will help your relative in the process of settling in. Relatives often have mixed feelings about staff. To see someone you care about being looked after by a 'stranger' is not easy. The more skilled and attentive the member of staff and the more trust your relative places in them, the harder it can be. However caring the staff, your place in your relative's life is special. What you share with them goes back many years and cannot be replaced.

Relatives do not always voice appreciation to staff, taking it for granted that staff realise how grateful they are. Staff tend to only hear the things they are doing wrong, not the things they do well. It may help to express thanks on behalf of your relative and show awareness of stresses of the job. A Christmas card, thank you note or box of chocolates or a vote of thanks at a meeting, will mean a great deal. For many staff, this is more than 'just a job'. They invest energy and imagination in caring for residents. Recognise their commitment through simple gestures.

As with all relationships, trust is central in dealings between relatives and staff in care homes. It might take a while before you feel entirely confident in staff but remember to do things and say things that convey trust. It can undermine relationships if relatives inadvertently do things that give the impression they are 'checking up' on staff.

Esther knew she should be glad, but she found it hard when staff said her dad Wesley was no trouble and that they enjoyed hearing about his days growing up in the Caribbean. She felt a failure, knowing how frustrating she had found caring for him at home as his dementia progressed. When staff said what a lovely person Wesley was, it only made her feel more guilty. Noticing she looked upset at the end of a visit, the cleaner Doris asked if she was all right. Doris reassured her that her dad thought the world of her. It was only natural she had found the stress of caring for him at home too difficult.

## Visiting preferences

Relatives are sometimes told by staff not to visit for the first few days and well meaning friends may imply it's time to move on, to build a 'new life' but only you can work out what is best. Some new residents are unsettled by early visits from family, others feel abandoned if they don't see close relatives.

123

Some relatives enjoy the freedom to do things they have not been able to do for a while whilst others can't imagine not spending time each day with the person who has moved into a home. Your visiting is likely to follow the pattern of contact you had with them before the move.

If you want to visit your relative every day, staff will welcome this. You might discover after a while that you feel relaxed about visiting less often, it's up to you. Most relatives visit less frequently than daily. Husbands and wives tend to visit very often. Weekly or fortnightly visits are common among sons and daughters. If you are in paid work, early evenings or weekends may be the best time to visit. If you have more freedom, good times tend to be mid morning and mid afternoon. Avoid mealtimes, unless you are going with the intention of helping or of sharing a meal, and avoid times when staff are very busy if you want to have time with them to catch up. Having said all this, there are no restrictions over visiting generally because the care home is a home not a hospital. Sometimes care home staff say 'just turn up' but knowing about a visit in advance can be helpful as the resident can look forward to the visit and staff can be prepared if they want to share information.

Staff will be able to give tips about the length and timing of your visits. They can observe when your relative tends to be most alert and able to converse. They may suggest visiting while an activity your relative enjoys is taking place, so you can enjoy it together. Frail older people have limited stamina, however much they enjoy seeing friends and family so it's best to be sensitive to signs they might be tiring. Your relative may not always seem as pleased to see you as you are hoping they will be. There are lots of possible reasons for this. They may be disorientated because of the newness of everything. They may subconsciously blame you for what has happened or they may be absorbed in what is going on at the time (an activity or a conversation). If you feel the need, talk with a member of staff.

Where you spend your visits is up to you and your relative. Don't feel awkward about asking staff to help move them to a quieter, more private part of the home, if this will be better for both of you. If you will always want to spend visits in your relative's room, let staff know so that they can be prepared. Some visitors enjoy spending time with their relative in the communal parts of the home so they can talk to other residents, people visiting at the same time and members of staff.

There may be a quiet lounge or a cluster of chairs you can retreat to or the garden. If you are visiting your partner, privacy may be a priority in enabling intimacy. You can close the bedroom door and ask not to be disturbed.

Strong links are often forged between relatives visiting older people in care homes. You may find you can talk to each other, understand and share some of the pressures of this stage of caring. Some people arrange to visit at the same time each week so they can meet up. Other residents may enjoy seeing you, too, and this contact with you can enrich the lives of people who may have few visitors.

It can feel strangely unnatural, visiting someone with whom you have a close and enduring relationship in this new setting under the watchful eyes of unfamiliar people. Conversation may be stilted and it is difficult knowing how best to spend the time together. So it helps to have a plan of things to do and share to avoid awkward silences and shortened visits. Why not try:

- looking at and sorting family photos
- looking at a book or magazine together
- playing cards or another board game
- tapping into your relative's memories to write up the family history
- writing a card or letter to another relative or friend
- sharing a picnic or edible treat (let staff know)
- going for a walk in the garden
- watching a DVD of a favourite TV programme or film
- doing things to enhance your resident's room, such as looking after pot plants.

If you are bringing in pictures and photos to look at, it helps if they are larger than 6×4 size, preferably A4, as this is easier to see. An ideal way of bringing interest and variety to visits is bringing in other family members or old neighbours or friends of your relative. This helps with the flow of conversation and will be especially meaningful if the other visitor is someone who might otherwise find it hard to visit. It will take some of the weight from you, too, and be a source of support and companionship in what can be a lonely role. Another sure-fire success in any care home is visiting with a pet or a young child. Older people can respond with heart-warming enthusiasm to the presence of a small baby or an animal such as a well-trained dog. Check with staff if you are planning on bringing in a pet or younger member of the family so they can be prepared.

## Going on trips and taking part in activities

Some visitors feel daunted at the prospect of going on outings with their relative. But with a bit of planning, it might be possible for you to take your relative to a local park, shopping centre, café or pub. Being able to go out is part of normal life and gives variety, something to look forward to. Staff can advise on transport and help you think through aspects of the trip (like using a wheelchair and any continence issues). On organised trips, staff, such as the activity co-ordinator, will be allocated to accompany residents. If the home is planning a trip, they will usually welcome friends and relatives to join in. This provides extra help and adds to everyone's enjoyment of the day. The same applies to events and activities taking place in the home. If you can plan your visits around these occasions it is a good way to encourage your relative to join in.

> Colin was finding visits to see his wife Emily difficult. She rarely had anything to report and, more often than not, he resorted to reading the paper after ten minutes. He was glad when Naomi, the home's activities organiser, asked if he would like to come on an outing she was planning to a local garden centre. Emily had been a keen gardener so he knew she would enjoy the visit. And it would be like old times looking round at the selection of plants followed by tea and cake in the café. It would be something positive to look forward to and would give Colin the added encouragement of feeling useful. Naomi had mentioned how helpful it was to have relatives come along as volunteers on trips.

## Getting information and keeping in touch

It is normal to feel out of touch with your relative's life when they move into a home. You go from knowing everything that is happening to feeling vague about details of their lives from day to day. This may leave you feeling vulnerable but there is no need for you to be out of touch. Although memory problems might make it difficult for you to ask your relative what has been happening, informing families is a key part of the staff's role.

It can seem as if staff are fully occupied, too busy to be interrupted. It is true that staff have lots of tasks to complete but keeping in touch with regular visitors is one of those tasks. Regular updates are useful for everyone. Staff can occasionally be hard to find (perhaps because they are giving personal care in a resident's room) but if you are patient, there will always be someone available. Talk with staff who work closely with your relative as they can give you an accurate picture. You can ask to see the care plan whenever you visit (provided your relative is happy for you to look at it). This will tell about your relative's health and well-being and records activities they have taken part in, how they have been eating and sleeping and so on.

In between visits, keep in touch by phoning or emailing the home. This is a vital channel of communication for families who live at a distance but can be useful for all of us with busy lives. Staff will welcome telephone and email enquiries. But don't expect all staff to be equally informed about your relative. The staff on their unit will be in the best position to give you an update.

You may have been used to supporting your relative during appointments with doctors and social services staff. If you would like to be present when they see a doctor or other health professional and your relative would like you there too, let the staff know. If you are not able to be present, staff will let you know the outcome. When the care manager arranges to see your relative for a review, they are likely to call you to fix a mutually convenient time. In between social services reviews, you may not have a named care manager but you can still request a meeting if the need arises.

## Relatives' meetings

It is now accepted practice for care homes to hold regular relatives' meetings as a way of keeping friends and family members involved. If you are able to attend, this can be a valuable point of contact with both staff and other visitors.

Meetings are useful for lots of reasons:

- they are a way of keeping relatives informed of news from the home
- they give a chance to ask questions
- they allow staff and relatives to share ideas for improving the home
- they often have a relevant topic or speaker and are an opportunity to understand more
- they are an opportunity for relatives to support each other
- they can help nip problems in the bud by allowing relatives to share concerns.

However relatives' meetings are not an appropriate place for sharing individual grievances. These are best addressed in meetings with staff for the sake of your relative's privacy.

Homes vary in the frequency with which they hold relatives' meeting. They may just plan a couple each year or they may have them as often as once every few weeks. Some homes hold meetings on weekday afternoons, some on weekday evenings and some at weekends, again to suit the needs of staff and visitors. Smaller homes struggle to make meetings viable. This is usually the reason a home does not have regular meetings. In other homes, the lifestyles of relatives makes it difficult. Or social events are seen as an alternative vehicle for involving relatives. There may also be a history of meetings not going well (turning into 'moans sessions') which can put staff off arranging further dates. Another reason meetings may not be happening is that previous meetings have been poorly attended by relatives. Sometimes relatives and staff have not grasped the potential benefits of having regular meetings.

Confident managers will be open to relatives sharing the running of relatives' meetings. It can be very positive for relatives to take the role of chair or secretary, for instance. It is not always easy to identify someone with the time and skills to take on these roles, however, so often they fall to staff. Some homes have partnerships with local organisations (such as Age Concern or the Alzheimer's Society) who help them run the group. In many ways, this is the ideal model for meetings. If you are not able to attend relatives' meetings, you can still find out what happened if the home produces notes of the meetings which are then circulated to all next of kin.

## Giving your suggestions

Visitors to care homes have a vital role to play in making sure standards in care homes are maintained. They can be a useful source of feedback to staff as they are not in the home all the time so can notice when things start to slip, even simple things like smells in different parts of the home which staff can become used to. The process of inspecting homes includes asking visitors (friends and family members as well as professionals who go in regularly) what they think of the quality of service provided. Between inspections, managers are asked to evaluate the service regularly. This process also includes collecting the views of friends and relatives.

Relatives' meetings are an opportunity to give your views, though these should be relevant to the home as a whole and not just things that concern your relative. You will also receive questionnaires from the Commission for Social Care Inspection (to be called the Care Quality Commission as of April 2009) and from the home itself. The questionnaires may ask you about specific areas of the service or they may cover all aspects of home life. If there is space, give additional comments as well as ticking boxes (if not, use extra paper if you feel you want to). The home may also have a 'comments book' or 'suggestions box', usually in the foyer. You can use this to let staff know your ideas for improving the service as well as to give positive feedback. You can make your comments anonymously if you wish but if you leave your name it will be easier for staff to follow up.

You may find it easier to speak with staff in person. Staff may be available when you visit or you could make an appointment to talk. Alternatively, you could write a letter, card or email expressing ideas. It can be a boost to staff if they receive a nice card praising them for the care they provide.

## Visiting someone with dementia

Visiting a person with dementia in a care home can be difficult and you are not alone if you feel daunted by the prospect. Conversation can be limited if the person's verbal communication skills are failing. It can be puzzling to know what to do during the visit. Your relative may not recognise you straight away or you may have a hurtful or unexpected reaction from them when you arrive.

Remember that your relative's world may have become smaller as a consequence of their dementia progressing. It might seem that the range of topics they are able to talk about is becoming narrower. Their memory problems can make it hard for them to answer questions about what they have done since your last visit. If you speak with staff before you go to your relative, they might be able to give you some ideas for jogging the person's memory about what they have done. Your relative may repeat questions like 'Why am I here?' or 'When am I going home?' a lot. Gently explaining or validating feelings each time may help lessen the confusion and anxiety. You can also divert the conversation to other topics. Try to avoid concealing the truth from your relative by telling them, for instance, that they will be going home soon. This is not fair to them and will make you feel bad too.

One of the greatest challenges when visiting a person with dementia is that you never know what will happen. 'Expect the unexpected' is good advice. People with dementia have good days and bad days, like the rest of us. Sometimes they may appear genuinely pleased to see you, other days less so. Hard though it is, the best approach is not to take hurtful responses personally. Your relative is not deliberately upsetting you.

A flashpoint in visiting can be getting ready to leave. Your relative may be upset you are going, or want you to take them with you. The visit can end on a distressing note. Plan your exit with staff if you fear this may happen. One strategy some visitors find effective is to leave just before a meal. Staff are then able to take the person to the dining room and engage them in something positive.

Don't feel you have to soldier on alone if visiting is hard. Staff in the home know how upsetting it can be, and will talk to you about your visits. You could also have a friend or relative you confide in when the going gets tough. Or ring one of the helplines listed at the back of the book.

## Caring from a distance

In our global society, many relatives and friends are supporting someone in a care home from a distance. This does not mean you can't be involved in their life. Your role in supporting the person is just as important as if you lived in the next street.

Ring your relative or friend at any time, though you may find it works better if there is a regular time when you phone so that staff are prepared and your relative can be reminded and have something to look forward to. Consider having a phone installed in their room or buying them a mobile phone (remember you may then be open to receiving calls at inopportune moments). Homes have to provide a phone residents can use privately. This might be a trolley or mobile phone. You will have to wait while staff take the phone to your relative so it might be as well to ring back a few minutes later. Discuss the times of day that are most convenient for speaking on the telephone with staff. In the future, a growing number of older people in care homes will have their own computers to help them keep in touch with family members. In the meantime, cards and letters are greatly valued. And staff can help your relative if they have difficulty reading.

Feel confident about ringing the home whenever you want information about your relative. Resist feeling a nuisance. If you ring at a busy moment, staff can always ask you to call back a little later. If there are going to be gaps of several months between your visits, you may find it helps to have a regular agreed time when you telephone or email for an update. They may also ring you with regular news. Don't be alarmed if staff call you. They will be in touch if there are changes in your relative's health or if they have a fall, an illness or an accident so don't assume the worst.

Making regular visits to a care home a long way from where you live can be draining, especially if you work during the week and visit at weekends. Be mindful of the impact on your health and energy levels. Some care homes can accommodate people who visit from a distance. There may be a guest room you can use for a modest charge. You may also be able to order a meal in advance. Some homes can prepare a dining table for the family in a private room so you can have a meal to celebrate your relative's birthday or an anniversary, for example.

# Summary

## Step Eight • Getting involved

- The care plan is the key document which will influence your relative's day-to-day experiences in the home. Get involved in writing it and keeping it up-to-date.

- Your relative's life history is something you alone can share, especially if they are limited in their verbal communication skills. Think through what staff could usefully be told about their life.

- Trusting relationships between family members and staff working in a care home need to be established on a good footing early on. This will help build a partnership approach.

- Visiting a relative or friend in a care home can be daunting. Plan visits and discuss ideas for spending time together with staff.

- Being kept in the picture is a necessary part of staying involved in a person's life after they move into a home. Work out the best ways to stay in touch.

- Make use of all opportunities to feedback ideas. Attending relatives' meetings is a good way of getting involved.

# Step Nine
# Dealing with problems and change

Relatives form a partnership with residents and staff in a care home. This is sometimes referred to as the 'relationship triangle'. When there are problems, give and take on both sides in a spirit of mutual respect is helpful. Significant problems may not necessarily occur. But given the nature and complexities around running, living in and visiting a care home, it is likely that concerns may arise.

Actively building up trust and positive relationships through good communication and constructive feedback lays the foundations for resolving issues early. Where there is a problem or differences of opinion, it is the quality of the relationship that will affect a satisfactory outcome. Most of the issues raised in this section will be supported by written policies and procedures within the home. You can ask to have these explained or view them yourself.

## Common areas of concern

Considering the high emotional investment involved with helping a relative settle into a care home, it's only natural that concerns may occasionally arise. Some of the areas which can cause problems for your relative or you include:

- a change of manager or owner
- a change of system or regulations
- high staff turnover or agency staff
- money running out
- a lack of clarity around costs or lack of adequate explanation
- changes in their medical condition
- lack of understanding of what is acceptable and reasonable to expect
- not being informed in a timely way about changes in the condition of your relative or issues affecting their health or well-being
- fears of abuse or lack of dignity within caring relationships
- your inability to visit regularly and keep an eye on things as you live too far away
- communication difficulties
- relationship problems
- lack of stimulation during the day
- concerns about care at night.

Should any of these occur try not to panic. This chapter deals with the procedures put in place to help you and your relative.

## Abuse matters

Research tells us that older people are more likely to experience abuse or mistreatment living in their own homes than in a more formal care setting. Cases do, nevertheless, occur in care homes. Take action promptly to ensure any abuse is not allowed to continue. Abuse can be any behaviour towards a person that causes them harm, endangers life or violates their rights.

**Examples of abuse include:**

- physical – hitting or shaking someone
- sexual – any sexual activity that a person does not understand or want
- psychological – threats of harm, abandonment, humiliation, intimidation or verbal abuse
- financial – stealing or denying access to money or possessions
- neglect – ignoring someone's medical or care needs or withholding food
- discrimination – on grounds of race, gender or disability
- institutional – abuse by an organisation imposing rigid and insensitive routines, unskilled, intrusive or invasive interventions or an environment allowing inadequate privacy or physical comfort.

If you are worried that someone you know could be abused, it is important to tell someone immediately. You can report your concerns directly to the manager of the home. If the person in charge is the abuser then report it to the Inspectorate or the proprietor. If you prefer, you can raise your concerns with your local authority's social services department. If you would like to discuss an issue with someone independently, call Action on Elder Abuse's Response Line (0808 808 4141). This is a freephone helpline for anyone concerned, in any way, about the abuse of older people. It is staffed by paid workers and volunteers who are trained and experienced in providing advice on abuse.

**Some symptoms of abuse are:**

- recurring unexplained injuries
- untreated injuries and medical problems
- frequent visits to A&E departments
- regular agitation and being emotionally upset
- poor hygiene or unchanged bedding
- wearing unsuitable clothing or clothing that is not their own
- unexplained weight loss or dehydration
- appearing withdrawn, depressed, agitated or fearful, sleeping irregularly or loss of appetite.

As the 'guardian' of your relative's welfare, it is important to be aware of signs should they arise. Any aspect of dignity can be a problem when staff are not adequately trained, there are language or communication barriers or there is insufficient leadership in 'person-centred' practice.

# Who protects older people living in care homes?

The inspectors regulate homes to published standards. If homes do not comply with them, they can issue an enforcement notice. In serious cases, this could lead to criminal convictions. Inspectors are able to close homes (although homes have the right to appeal). However, the Inspectorate does not act as an adult protection police force nor does it pursue individual complaints, although it will investigate where there is an allegation of a serious breach of regulation.

Where there are concerns about an individual's professional behaviour (based on the professional codes of conduct of registered nurses) this is regulated by the Nursing and Midwifery Council. But it does not consider itself to be the primary agency concerned with adult protection. When a serious allegation has been reported, it has the power to suspend a member of staff from the home until the outcome of the case is known. There is a social care workers' code of conduct for unqualified staff through the General Social Care Council.

Where there is evidence of deliberate assault, the police get involved to investigate the case. But the majority of the responsibility for individual residents in nursing homes goes to social services. They will have an adult protection committee with broad representation from agencies involved with older people. In addition, in cases of poor practice, they have the power to terminate a contract with a care home where compliance has been breached. Any concerns should be raised with the local Protection of Vulnerable Adults (POVA) co-ordinator for further investigations (although individual local authorities will have their own policies and procedures). Residents are protected in that the homes' staff have to have CRB/POVA checks prior to being able to work there.

If you have concerns:

- visit at different times of the day or evening to see other aspects of your relative's care
- if your relative has given permission, or you have Power of Attorney, take an interest in the care plan. This should be reviewed regularly
- speak to other residents and relatives or join the relatives' group where you can share your experiences constructively and learn from others' experiences

- keep the lines of communication open with the home. Arrange to see the person in charge of the care of your relative face to face to discuss changes

- raise a concern or complaint with the home management as soon as possible

- contact the Relatives & Residents Association helpline for guidance

- if an issue is not resolved to your satisfaction, firstly report it to the inspectorate. After this there is the option of moving your relative to another home. However, this needs to be very carefully considered (due to evidence that suggests there is a substantial health risk involved with moving very frail older people from one home to another)

- before jumping to any conclusion, make sure you have all the facts. An abuse claim is very serious and starts a chain of events. You may find yourself part of a serious allegation in no time.

## Complaints and raising concerns

A good home will listen carefully to relatives and welcome suggestions. They won't take a defensive line to concerns or complaints. They will even encourage people to raise concerns openly as a way of helping them to improve their service. It can be the little things that matter most. It is important that you familiarise yourself with the complaints procedure when you first go into the home. Some homes issue 'untoward report' forms for when something needs to be highlighted in writing but it may not necessarily be a complaint.

Things you can do:

- start with positive approach. State the problem and agree a time when it can be resolved. Getting an agreement in the timescale gives you a reason to go back and follow it up

- try to build up positive relationships (avoid becoming a 'vexatious' visitor who complains constantly and makes unreasonable demands)

- even when things go wrong, go in with a smile on your face to prevent defensive or negative responses. Choose the best time to see the person in charge so they too have time to listen and talk calmly about the concern.

Badly handled situations can have a very demoralising effect on the staff and can damage the potential of everyone working together as partners. This is not to say that when serious concerns arise they should not be followed up. However, as with other types of communication, it is better to take a proactive positive approach. Always act in the best interests of your relative. If you are an expert or a professional with experience in this sector, your approach needs to be constructive and non-confrontational as it is easy for people to feel threatened by 'experts'. Be sensible and try to focus on what you are trying to achieve. Unfortunately, as things stand at present, there is little help outside the home to help deal with individual complaints for 'self-funding' residents. Therefore taking a co-operative approach, listening and seeing things from the home's perspective as well can help things along to a positive resolution.

- make notes and state times of any incidents as this is required for homes to follow up and trace back their records for that time

- it is easy to be 'wrong footed'. Think twice about the nature of the complaint and its importance to your relative. If you are seen to complain about petty things in an unreasonable way, it will be more of a challenge to get a successful resolution about things that really matter when they occur. Think about what you want to achieve. Is it better to 'win the battle and lose the war'?

- modify your approach to the desired outcome to keep your relative secure and safe where they can retain their identity. Help them continue living a life with purpose and a sense of achievement and meaning.

## What to do if you have a problem

- Discuss the concern with the person closest to the care of your relative (such as a key worker).
- Discuss the problem with the team leader.
- If you don't get a satisfactory response, talk it over with the manager.
- Complete an 'untoward events' form (if there is one) or take the formal complaint route.
- Involve senior management, the owner/proprietor or chief executive officer/managing director.

Always try to deal with problems locally before skipping to a last resort option.

Remember, you can contact the Relatives & Residents Association Helpline to guide you through any stage of the above (see **Appendix 2** for contact information).

We shall tackle some of these issues or 'signpost' you to experts already out there to give advice.

# Health and care issues

## Balancing risk

Care homes undertake individual risk assessments which should focus on enabling people to live their lives and maximise their strengths. Getting the balance right between an activity which has an element of risk with a duty of care requires skill. It is never possible to eliminate all risks but the aim should be to minimise danger and harm by making decisions based on a good quality of life and the resident's best interests. Think about what your relative needs in terms of continuity of lifestyle, security, dignity and independence. Keeping active and challenged is important for many care home residents. In a situation of potential harm, the assessment of risk considers ways of reducing the risk at the same time as enabling a person to continue to have quality of life.

Jack is an 87 year old who has lived in a residential care home for the past three years. He is able to walk unaided for short distances but has begun to experience some episodes of memory loss. Through discussions with Jack, it was discovered that he enjoys walking (he used to have a dog), getting out and about and having some routine. Staff devised a selection of motivating activity 'targets' to improve his levels of physical activity. His new routine includes walks to the post-box and a local pub with a member of staff accompanied by a friend on the way home. When his family visits, they ask him if he has met his 'targets' for that day. He enjoys working towards improvements in his general mobility as it helps him to maintain independence.

With lots of positive feedback and interest from the family and staff, the new routine has increased his self-esteem. It keeps him motivated. The improvement in his walking capability has been noticed. The activity co-ordinator contacted the local RSPCA and, with the help of a staff member, he is now able to participate in a dog walking scheme.

It is easy to become overprotective and wrap your relative in cotton wool, with the best of caring intentions. However, this can stifle their individuality and sense of being in control of their lives. Duty of care comes into play when a person is likely to do something of harm to themselves or others.

Restraint includes any action or control which restricts a person from doing something as part of risk management. Person-centred approaches to risk try to avoid using restraint. The home policies should be clear about this. Restraint normally falls into three types, physical, chemical or emotional. Here are some examples:

- **physical** – preventing a resident from getting up from a chair by putting a fixed tray in front of them, locking people in or out of rooms or putting barriers in front of doorways
- **chemical** – using sedative drugs
- **emotional** – deceiving, shouting, offering no choice or control, isolating or ignoring a resident.

The use of 'smart technology' for door sensors, alarms or forms of tagging always encourages debate and review. A balance of the needs of the individual and the whole community has to be considered in finding the best approach. However, technology should not be used to reduce staff hours, replace human interaction and communication or intrude into individual privacy.

Most situations need to be balanced according to the impact on your relative's physical condition, psychological state, social or emotional needs. The key word in risk taking is 'negotiate'. Think about all the needs of your relative (not just the physical).

## Customs and cultural difficulties

Language and culture differences are an increasing issue in care homes. It is important for relatives to consider the way information is shared about their relative's preferences and every-day routines to make the care 'person-centred'.

Expect a reasonable use of English from the staff. Use of pictures and demonstrating with simple verbal instructions can help to ensure staff understand your relative and what matters to them.

It is easy for little things to cause a problem requiring patience, perseverance and a positive approach towards the care staff. Where a key worker system is in place, it is easier to discuss these things with them and rely on them to explain to the rest of the care team.

> Carol's father Sid had a stroke. He had parted his hair on the right side for the last 30 years. One day, when Carol came to visit her father and staff directed her to him, she exclaimed, 'That's not my father!' He looked so different. She realised that staff had not understood the importance of this to him. When Carol explained it to them, it went into the care plan.

Some staff may view small matters differently. Gently remind them of what was customary and normal for your relative. Use your knowledge for guidance to help rather than 'having a go' at the staff. They may be doing something they see as quite acceptable.

## Health issues

Concerns might include such issues as pressure sores, medication, management of incontinence and levels of cleanliness. These can directly relate to staff training and resourcing, leadership and having the right support from specialist health professionals. Regulations state that there should be adequate staffing to meet the needs of residents. If you have concerns, raise them with the home. If you don't get a satisfactory response, it can be discussed with the Inspectorate (to be called the Care Quality Commission as of April 2009) for clarification.

It is better to sort things out with the staff as a health concern arises. As many visiting relatives adopt a monitoring role, it is important that lines of communication and involvement in care planning are worked out. Access to appropriate health professionals can vary according to the policy of the local Primary Care Trust and the relationship the home has with local services. It is important that the home presses for the outside expertise it needs from the local health professionals.

## Medication

Many residents have a complex range of medicines to take daily. These need to be reviewed regularly by a doctor or pharmacist. Difficulties may arise if a resident refuses to take tablets or when liquid alternatives are not available. The GP and family might get involved if other solutions are considered requiring a risk assessment.

There are strict rules on keeping records and ensuring staff are properly trained to administer drugs. Even if you take your relative out for the day, the home fills in a form when it gives you the medicine to ensure your relative is taking the right dose at the right time.

Side effects can create their own problems (such as nausea, constipation or sleepiness). Sometimes, medication is given to settle someone whose behaviour might be seen as challenging (particularly where there are mental health difficulties although most of this behaviour is situation specific). In many cases, there are alternatives to giving tranquillisers. They should only be used as a last resort. It requires a sensitive approach which considers individual needs, provides opportunities for social activity, and involves empathy and good communication skills. Staff need specific training to work with people with dementia. In respect of pain, dealing with residents who have dementia, learning difficulties or strokes where communication is a problem, the use of pain assessment tools is particularly important. Observing body language or using picture images can help to identify, monitor and control pain. Make sure staff know your relative's past medical history if any of it could impinge on their present medical problems. Though not necessarily raised on admission, this knowledge may make a lot of difference. It can affect how care can improve quality of life, particularly for those with problems like arthritis and angina. Behaviour problems can stem from undetected pain in people with dementia. Staff need as much information as possible to understand how someone communicates pain or mental stress.

## Night time

Sleep can be a problem for some residents. Outside disturbances can make a situation worse but most of these can be resolved where there is a creative and responsive management. Difficulties sleeping can be tackled depending on the cause of the problem.

External disturbances can be simple (such as lights in corridors to assist night staff, call bells, loud residents, a resident wandering out of their room, doors banging or even phones ringing). Some residents can be frightened by unexplained, unfamiliar sounds or interruptions. Any concern needs to be raised with the person in charge. Person-centred care plans deal specifically with night time habits (such as use of music, TV, specific drinks, lavender and evening baths) to prevent unnecessary use of medication. Additional information from relatives about how a resident formerly managed at home can help avoid night sedation.

# Relationship and communication difficulties

## Expectations

It is easy to become 'unstuck' if these are not realistic. The level of personal care and staff input to your relative needs to be understood at the beginning. Guilt can often express itself through unrealistic expectations of how much can reasonably be provided. Good homes take into account the physical, social and emotional needs of residents but it is helpful to know to what extent it is provided. You can then negotiate or supplement with 'extras' which can make all the difference (such as going for a daily walk, or having additional support with a hobby, or looking after a pet which is over and above what is normally provided). Again, prompt communication of the issue at the earliest stage, to prevent disappointment, misunderstanding or any deterioration is essential.

## Understand boundaries

Consider how much involvement you and your relative may wish to have regarding different aspects of care and daily life in the home. Most homes aim to provide care tailored to the individual. In partnership with relatives, this must be balanced with the needs of other residents in the home. This requires good leadership, communication and relationships.

The level of involvement in the community life of the home will vary, although most residents benefit from a strong sense of community. There is a difference between the public 'community' home life and the 'private life' of a resident. The balance will be determined by what your relative needs as well as the culture of the home.

# Intimacy

Human intimacy is a basic need throughout life and an important means of communication. Old age does not stop a person responding in a romantic, sensual or sexual way to others. The opportunity for physical contact may be limited by physical disability or pain restricting movement and the ability to meet people. Although a resident may have lived alone for 10–15 years prior to coming into the home, it is not impossible for relationships to develop given the right mix of people. For some people, a care home can be a place of unexpected opportunities to meet people and enjoy a new set of relationship possibilities with those around them.

Some will have the energy and interest to let intimate relationships develop. You may find the idea of an emotional attachment with someone outside the family hub unlikely or unacceptable. It is important to think of the needs of your relative and what is appropriate for them. If they have dementia, staff will probably tell you early on if a new relationship is forming. This will allow you time to think it through. Sometimes residents can misinterpret behaviour. You can help by talking things over with them to help them to put it in perspective. For example, with same sex relationships, things need to be addressed early on to clarify expectations as to how this aspect of the relationship should be managed.

Example of challenges include:

- **flirtatious residents** – when this happens it is not surprising, especially as most homes are female dominated and men are in a minority. It can bring people back to life and be highly motivating

- **protective spouses** – some spouses can be very protective of each other, particularly if their partner becomes friendly with other residents. Jealousies can occur but this rather depends on the relationship and level of understanding of the partner concerned

- **mistaken identity** – sometimes, people with dementia can misinterpret a person for someone they once knew and this can be a problem in extreme cases. As a last resort, one of the residents involved may need to move to a different home.

Possible solutions:

- finding friendship and showing warm gestures of physical affection shared between residents and staff can help to meet emotional needs for intimacy and love. This must not be confused with 'abuse' which, like avoiding any risk, can be taken too far. If the pendulum swings too far one way problems arise. A reasoned, balanced approach serves the best interests of all concerned

- forming attachments with pets where homes have them

- looking after plants or being enabled to contribute and give care by listening and offering support to another resident, member of staff or relative in some way. This channels energies and meets the need for giving and receiving, contributing to the well-being of another person

- help your relative to feel attractive by continuing to take an interest in their appearance as they did before. Renew lipsticks, scents or other customary cosmetics. For men, use the right aftershave, and make sure they are well shaved or have a tie of their choice

- look at the home's policy guidelines on personal and sexual relationships. Staff are given clear guidelines about how to respond to different types of behaviour.

## Staff problems

You always hope to select a home where there is stable management. A fast turnover of a home manager does not bode well for quality and creates insecurity and discontinuity for residents, staff and visiting relatives (although this can vary around the country. High turnovers are common in London). There will be occasions when ownership or managers change and families need to be aware of the impact. This can alter the way care is organised or resourced, the way the home is administered or the approach to certain aspects of care or activity.

Essex Heights care home had recently replaced the manager. It became apparent to the visiting relatives and the other members of the staff that things were not as they appeared to be. The new manager had problems with her mood, consistency, appeared distant and was often unreliable. She was clearly not performing to expectations and standards and this had an immediate effect on the residents, their moods and sense of well-being. Once the matter was dealt with and the manager was replaced, things settled down.

The residents (most of whom had dementia) seemed to relax as the staff and those around them gradually regained confidence in the new manager. It was like a completely different place and demonstrated how much influence a manager has on the culture and atmosphere of a home.

Other problems may include staff lacking commitment or interest in the job. In some homes, because of different working and resourcing arrangements, staff may work long hours. This can make them susceptible to 'burn-out' if they are not well supported, equipped and valued. Sometimes, problems arise if they volunteer to work long hours to earn more money. This can result in fatigue, affecting the quality of care given. If you notice symptoms or have concerns, bring these to the attention of the manager.

A lack of key worker or 'named' member of staff in charge of a particular group of residents, taking particular interest in their care and welfare, can create uncertainty for relatives and residents. Knowing who is responsible for different aspects of care helps to relieve anxieties when they arise.

It is also helpful for relatives (as well as staff) to know more about medical conditions and their effects on residents (such as pain, arthritis, Parkinson's, sensory or memory difficulties). Having opportunities to learn about these conditions helps understanding. Some homes cover these aspects in relatives' meetings where there is a specific interest.

Having the right staffing levels to meet constantly changing needs and using agency staff poses challenges to care homes. It needs a delicate balancing act in staff deployment. Being able to recruit suitable staff and retain them is a major challenge for some homes. You may be justifiably concerned if there is a high turnover affecting continuity and stability. If staff are tired or over-worked and their needs not attended to, it is natural that staff motivation and job satisfaction will be compromised. Staff need to feel supported and appreciated by visitors as well as others. Show that you understand some of the constraints which staff operate under. Contented staff make an important contribution to the well-being of residents and the home's atmosphere. Your support can provide a huge boost to their morale.

You should, however, feel able to raise concerns about staff if there is an issue affecting your relative's well-being. You are their 'eyes and ears'. Have an active interest in staff and keep lines of communication open.

These days, care home workforces represent a range of cultures. This can provide a rich and interesting diversity but can sometimes be a cause of tensions. The finer points of national character, culture and individual difference of your relative may not always be understood by some staff from different cultures.

In addition, the momentous cultural and attitude changes experienced during the lifetime of an older generation may leave some residents bewildered when the way they like to do things and the finer points of communication are not understood or responded to in familiar ways. Some residents will not fall in line with a politically correct view point and this forms part of the staff preparation. Providing a life story to explain the life and ways of your relative clearly can improve understanding. Ideally, there will be additional training on cultural issues. This is a sensitive area but one which some homes need to address.

## Other issues you may need to think about

## Moving to a new home

Moving home for whatever reason is stressful. It can be the result of high levels of anxiety about a care home, a break-down of trust or, most commonly, due to changing needs of the resident (if the staff are not trained to support these). Most homes try to avoid this and, in some cases, there may be a specialist unit to help make the transition easier. Any decisions should be taken on the basis of their well-being. The needs of your relative should be informed by professional advice.

The impact a move can have will depend on the condition of your relative and the way the move is planned and managed. Residents occasionally have to move 'en bloc' to another care home while their home is being refurbished to get away from the disruption or noise. A home might close. There are more unusual reasons for residents needing to move, such as flood damage. Where possible, prepare your relative carefully and make sure you both understand what is happening at each step of the way. Moving requires careful handling and understanding with plenty of information. There will be special meetings for residents and relatives to iron out misunderstandings or anxieties and provide reassurance for continued well-being. The continuity of care and safety of personal belongings, or dealing with anxieties (such as staffing arrangements) all need to be addressed. A good home will manage these issues and make arrangements for staff to remain constant to provide some sense of continuity and security for residents. If a home temporarily relocates with a group of residents, your relative's involvement is important. Some residents may need careful one to one discussions and support through this unsettling time. This is particularly difficult for people with dementia who may be dependent on trusting relationships and familiarity for their security.

> Alfred was very fond of Jo, his key worker. When he found out the home was being refurbished and that he would need to move to another home nearby, the thing that most concerned him was losing the person who understood his painful arthritis and how to help move him to prevent pain. He was delighted when the home management arranged for Jo to work at the home for this period. They were grateful to take on a member of staff who knew the six residents moving there for the interim period.

## Conflict in the wider family

Difficulties can arise in families at key decision points in parents' lives when they become frail and need active intervention from their families. Differing attitudes, beliefs and experiences can end in conflict. A time of change (such as deterioration in the health of your relative) may affect responsibilities. Someone will need to take a negotiating role, focusing on the best interests of the relative you are supporting. Sometimes, difficulties occur in emotionally charged circumstances.

It is hard to be objective, particularly where guilt or blame are involved. Try to take time to reflect before acting and getting all the facts from the different perspectives. Be prepared with all the facts to hand. Work within the 'possible' solutions and there is more likely to be a better outcome. Where there is a difficult relationship 'heritage' within a family, it might be helpful to get 'outside' help, support or mediation.

## If the money runs out

This can creep up on people as no one knows how long your relative will need the care home. When money runs out, normally social services will get involved.

They will discuss the situation with the home. They tend to pay the home less than people who pay privately. If the difference between their rates and the home's charges is too great, the home might suggest a cheaper room, or approaching a third party for 'top ups' if additional services are necessary. A third party is only sought where genuinely preferred accommodation is required. Social services will not pay more than the usual cost (taking into consideration the assessed needs. Top ups can feel like emotional blackmail to some relatives who do not want to disrupt the lives of their relative by moving them on. But while the financing of care homes is in such a muddle, it is an area that will continue to vary according to the area you live and appear unfair and inconsistent. Some homes will take a compassionate view and accept the local authority rates.

Before any change in the service, such as moving, you should insist on a full social services assessment that takes account of social and psychological needs, risks to important social relationships and the effect of moving (get an independent medical opinion on the latter). If the local authority drags its feet on this make a formal complaint, go to the Ombudsman or consider legal action (it could be perceived as a failure to comply with community care law and failure to respect the person's human rights).

The CRAG (the Charging for Residential Accommodation Guide) 'disregard rules' mean that capital below £13,000 must be disregarded for the purpose of the means test for provision for residential care by the local authority. However, if you know capital is getting below £22,250, contact social services to ensure appropriate arrangements can be made before it's too late.

## Where to go for an independent listening ear

The Relatives & Residents Association advice line (020 7359 8136) is there to listen and offer empathetic understanding, giving callers the time to tell their story. Many callers feel let down by the system. They have experienced a roller coaster of emotions and inconsistent advice. The right information, advice and a warm listening ear will help you face your problems with more confidence and determination to continue down a particular path or pursue a course of action.

Their usual range of queries includes the selection of a home, funding, personal assessments and care plans, quality of life, abuse, complaints, activities and standards or issues around hospital discharge.

See **Appendix 1** for a range of best practice resources of interest to relatives involved with care homes.

# Summary

## Step Nine ● Dealing with problems and change

- Your involvement is critical for good care planning. Providing helpful information can prevent problems occurring, especially if your relative has memory or communication difficulties.

- It's always best to take a proactive and constructive approach to difficulties. Homes will benefit from constructive suggestions and good homes welcome helpful contributions from relatives.

- There are existing formal routes to follow if abuse is suspected. Familiarise yourself with the home's complaints process without fear of retribution – understanding roles, boundaries and what is reasonable to expect is important when negotiating changes or matters affecting your relative.

# Step Ten
# End of life

It is painful to think about the end of a person's life when they are beginning a new life in a care home. But being prepared will help you cope with the stress and heartache that this stage of supporting them may bring. Find ways to discuss your relative's wishes with them early on. This will give you a clearer sense of steps to take in the future.

As well as thinking about your relative's needs at the end of life, remember to take your own feelings into account. These are likely to be heightened as you face losing a person who has been a central part of your life, in all likelihood, for very many years.

## The grieving process

The grieving process does not always begin after a person close to you has died. If there has been a period of months (or even years) of poor health before they die, you began to 'lose' the person you knew even while they were still alive. Over time, you may find that your mum or dad is different in their relationship with you. It may feel as if you have switched roles, that you are now the parent and they are the child. If you are supporting your partner, you may miss the support and advice they always gave in the past. You miss the person they used to be. One of the stages in your journey of loss was the finality of them moving to a care home. Some say this is just as painful as when the person eventually dies.

## The 'long bereavement' of dementia care

This is especially the case when a person has dementia. From the moment you first notice changes in the person, right up to the day they actually die, you are gradually saying goodbye to them. Some people even say 'he isn't my dad any more', 'she's not the woman I married' or 'it's just the shell of who she was'. The experience of supporting someone through their dementia has been described as a 'long bereavement' with stages marked by specific losses and sadness. Dementia does have a recognised palliative stage when they are immobile and bed bound, drowsy for long periods, uninterested in food and drink, unable to swallow medication and prone to infection. Being bed bound leaves a person vulnerable to complications such as pressure sores. Pain may be a constant companion yet the person struggles to indicate this to those around them.

## Recognising and accepting signs of grief in your relative

You are not the only one going through the grieving process. Your relative is also likely to have feelings of loss. They have had to leave their home and come to terms with the loss of health and independence as well as going through bereavement often connected with the need for permanent care. Tearfulness, anger and lethargy are understandable. Give them time to work through their feelings, listening patiently.

## Giving your relative or friend the opportunity to talking about dying

Death is a 'taboo' subject in our culture. We don't find it easy to talk about dying and we tend to avoid conversations about it if possible. Some older people nearing the end of their lives do want to discuss it, however. It is helpful if they have the opportunity to talk openly rather than having to bottle up feelings because others are uncomfortable. Tread carefully, giving them a chance to open up if they want without forcing them to share their deepest feelings. You may discover that your relative has quite clear ideas about what they want to happen when they die (how they want their funeral arranged and what they would like to happen to their possessions).

There are spiritual needs that might need to be met, too. This may involve talking through what they believe and arranging for them to speak to someone who can help. It might be more about sorting out relationships and saying things that need to be said.

## Expressing your own grief

Being aware of your own grief reactions and understanding where they are coming from will help you to cope with them. Recognising that you are entering a period of painful change and loss, which brings lots of deep emotions, will enable you to take care of yourself and accept your feelings for what they are.

## Making your relative's wishes known

It might come as a shock when staff in the home raise questions early on about wishes for your relative's final days and after they die. This is something they have to do, however. It is a necessary part of the process of putting the care plan in place. Your relative may have prepared an advance care statement about what they want to happen in their final days. Were the person to die before this information has been gleaned, it would be impossible for staff to ensure their wishes were carried out.

## Finding ways to talk with your relative about their wishes

Hopes and choices for the end of life are not subjects you can raise carelessly. Build up gently to the conversation (if possible, well before the person moves into a care home).

Have the discussion on several occasions so you can be sure you have grasped what they want. If you feel your relative will not be comfortable talking with you about their wishes, is there someone else in whom they are likely to confide? A trusted friend or member of the local community? You might need to settle your relative's mind if they suspect the reason you are asking them is because you know something about their state of health. Reassure them this is 'standard procedure'. Part of the information the home has to collect.

## Information you need to pass on about your relative's wishes (such as faith and culture)

There are several key areas staff need to be informed about:

- do they want to be buried or cremated?
- who should be informed if they are in their final hours?
- have they paid in advance for a funeral plan, setting out their wishes?
- have they expressed a wish to die in a particular place (such as a hospice)?
- what are their beliefs? Is there a faith leader to contact when they are dying?
- are their cultural issues (such as prayers to be read, rules over who touches the body)?
- are there rituals to perform, and issues over the timing of burial or cremation?
- have they made specific requests (such as not wanting to be left alone)?
- are there objects of meaning (or certain individuals) they want with them?

## Telling the home when to contact you if the person is near death

Think things through before staff talk to you. How do you want them to manage your relative's final weeks, days and hours? If your relative took a turn for the worse during the night, do you want to be roused from sleep? Would you want to keep a bedside vigil in the final hours of their life? Are there other family members who would want to be there, too? Avoid pressure to conform to what you imagine is the 'right thing' to do in these circumstances. You alone know what will be most helpful for you and your relative.

## Procedures around death

A particularly painful area staff have to consult families over is whether or not to resuscitate their relative if their heart were to stop beating. With very frail older people, many families providing they hold Power of Attorney for making welfare decisions, opt to have a 'do not resuscitate' order in their relative's care plan if they lack the capacity to decide for themselves. They feel that it is more dignified to let nature take its course, especially if they have seen their relative enduring suffering. If staff find a resident has stopped breathing, they may otherwise call emergency services. Ambulance crews have to try to restart the heart which may just be delaying the inevitable. There are other ways of keeping a person alive longer. These include using antibiotics to combat an infection that might otherwise end someone's life or feeding them artificially when they have stopped eating. Ask staff to explain the decisions they are faced with so that you can guide them through in meeting the needs of your relative and the family.

# Finding acceptance

Even if you have had some time to prepare for your relative dying, the pain of losing them is likely to hit hard. It is the final hurdle in what has already been a stressful and upsetting phase of life.

## Stages of grief and loss

Your initial reaction to your relative's death may be complex. If they have been in pain, you are likely to feel some relief that they are free from the suffering. This relief may give you guilt. Grief and loss studies show that people tend to go through stages after the death of a person close to them. Not everyone experiences the stages in the same order. You might not experience all of the stages but a likely sequence is:

- **shock** – the reality may take time to sink in and people differ in their reaction to shock

- **denial** – difficulty grasping reality can lead to denial, not accepting what has happened

- **anger** – the realisation and the impact of loss can lead to anger 'why me?' or 'how will I cope?' or resentment and even jealousy of and blaming others

- **bargaining** – like having a conversation with yourself – 'if I do this or that the whole thing may go away'

- **despair** – feeling overwhelmed by the pain and hurt of the loss and feeling in the depths of emotional emptiness. Weeping and withdrawing from company is common
- **gathering/re-organising** – gradually the bereaved person may start to adjust by feeling able to take small steps towards their former life and routine, or new routines may help
- **acceptance** – through small steps you reach a level of awareness and understanding. Although the loss leaves a gap, you have adapted and found a way to live with the gap.

## Reflecting on experiences in the home

As you learn to live without your relative or friend, you will probably look back on the time they spent in the home with mixed feelings. Finding a way of accepting that phase of their life as having been necessary is part of moving on through the stages of your grief. During the angry and despairing phases of grief, you might find you blame yourself for things that happened that caused your relative suffering ('If only I had been able to keep him at home, his final days would have been easier…') Self-recrimination does not achieve anything. Take the reassurance offered by friends and relatives who are likely to be telling you that you did the right thing.

## Seeking support

Many people in the throes of grief seek counselling and support from organisations which specialise in helping bereaved people. The national charity for bereavement care is Cruse (phone 0844 477 9400 or visit www.crusebereavementcare.org.uk) but there will be local groups too. Support groups are useful for some people. For others, talking with close friends and relatives is the best way to work through the many feelings associated with losing someone.

## Keeping in touch with the care home

When your relative has died, you can feel you have lost a network of friendship and support at the care home. You may have become close to other residents, visitors and staff. Some people find it too painful to continue visiting the home, because of the reminders of the person they have lost. But others find it a comfort and a positive focus to keep up the links with people in the home (for instance by going to parties and social events).

# What to expect in the final days

It is not easy to be fully prepared for the experience of someone close to you dying, but you might find it useful to be aware of some of the things that may happen.

## Signs, symptoms and ways to relieve these

When people are in their final days and hours, some symptoms and signs that they are dying can be distressing for others to watch. These include:

- weakness
- fatigue
- shortness of breath or changed breathing patterns
- chest secretions
- anxiety/fear
- delirium
- feeling sick
- anorexia
- weight loss
- poor swallowing
- dry and sore mouth
- reduced fluid intake/dehydration
- muscle twitches, spasms and seizures
- failure of circulation
- withdrawal.

Adapted from Beckerman, D, *How to Have a Good Death*, Dorling Kindersley (2006), Chapter 1.

## Keeping a bedside vigil

If you would like to stay with your relative in their final hours, you can do this. It is a personal choice and you should not feel pressured. Staff will give discrete and sensitive support such as offering you a drink or snack, perhaps a blanket, even a bedroom where you can have a few hours' sleep if one is available. If you are not able to stay at your relative's bedside constantly, it is normal practice for care homes to ensure staff stay with a resident they know is dying. They understand that most people prefer not to die alone. Other members of the family and friends may want to share in the final hours of your relative's life and your relative might want to see certain people too.

## What is 'good practice?'

There are national protocols for looking after people who are dying (you might hear staff mention the 'Liverpool Care Pathway' or the 'Gold Standards Framework'). It is vital older people in care homes benefit from the excellent work being done in the palliative care world to relieve suffering. The National Council for Palliative Care has a project looking at the palliative care needs of people in the final stages of dementia and highlighting best practice. To find out more, visit their website (www.ncpc.org.uk) and click on the dementia project link.

It is not necessary for care homes to register a bed for palliative care if a resident is terminally ill (either through a terminal illness like cancer or heart failure) or because they are in the final stages of dementia. Many residents spend their final days in the home and this is the wish of most families. Having them admitted to hospital when they are dying can lead to person having a more upsetting death. Although they do not have to register beds for palliative care, homes are, however, asked to link with specialist palliative care teams when they need help and advice. They are expected to provide staff training on end of life care (though in some homes many staff have learned palliative care skills 'on the job'). When it is recognised that a resident is in their final days, staff may call a terminal stage care conference to discuss roles and expectations with the family. They may also involve palliative care specialists to advise on pain relief and control of symptoms.

People involved in supporting care homes through palliative care vary from area to area. Many hospices have outreach teams with nurses training and supporting care home staff. Community nursing teams (or Macmillan or Marie Curie nursing teams) often have a lead person to advise and implement best practice in end of life care. This might involve setting up intravenous pain relief (a syringe driver) or obtaining the right equipment to make a person comfortable (such as a mattress for their bed which will help prevent pressure sores).

## What happens when the person dies – who does what?

Most care homes have information on end of life issues which they can pass on to families. They may have leaflets or booklets explaining the processes and giving useful contact numbers. When a resident dies, staff must note the time and check for vital signs. They will contact the resident's next of kin immediately.

If the death was expected they notify the GP who will come to the home to certify the death. In a nursing home, two qualified nurses (one of whom has been certified as competent) may verify the death with the approval of the GP. They arrange for the body to be taken. Staff will contact the resident's chosen funeral director. They must also note the date, time and cause of death in the resident's care plan and notify the inspection team.

## Sudden death and expected death – the different rules

If someone dies suddenly and unexpectedly, staff must summon help using the local emergency system (calling for an ambulance, contacting the police and the resident's GP). The person cannot be removed from the home, unless resuscitation is appropriate, until the police give permission. The coroner will be informed as a post mortem will be carried out. They will give permission for the body to be taken away. As in expected deaths, staff must record the date, time and cause of death, together with the circumstances. They also have to inform the inspection body.

## Informing other residents and their visitors when someone dies

Homes have different practices for marking the death of a resident. There are various methods of informing visitors tactfully. Regular visitors will notice the person is not there and might want to pay their respects. Telling residents is more difficult for staff, especially when residents have memory problems. They may not remember the information so keep asking for the person who has died. Staff have to decide what will be best for each person but keeping the death from residents can have unfortunate consequences, such as causing anxiety or futile hope that the person will return. Losing a friend in the care home is a major event for a resident. The empty chair telling them the person is no longer there can be a painful reminder of their loss.

## Funeral arrangements – the role of the care home

Many care homes play a part in the funerals of their residents. Staff have built close bonds with residents and like to have an opportunity to say goodbye. Several members of staff may attend the service. Some homes can offer help in providing refreshments after the service. There may be regular occasions in the life of the home when residents who have died are remembered (such as an annual memorial service).

# Summary

## Step Ten • End of life

- Grief is something you can experience even before the person close to you dies.

- Changes in your relationship with them, in their abilities or personality can all trigger sadness. Seeing them move into a care home may be one of the stages of grief.

- Encourage your relative to express their feelings and wishes over the end of their life. This will enable you to know how to support and respect them when the time comes. These conversations need sensitive handling. It is especially vital that staff know about culture and faith based practices when the person is dying.

- The end of your relative's life may be distressing to watch. It is important to be aware of your own feelings.

- Close partnership between relatives and staff is important to set the right tone for your relative. Sharing the tasks and supporting each other will help make the experience as positive as possible for everyone.

- Your relationship with the care home does not have to end after your relative has died. If you find it helpful and comforting as you move through the grieving process, keep in touch with staff and pop in from time to time.

## Dedication

This book is dedicated to Rosemary's mother, Edith Brooking –
as a representative of the thousands of residents in
care homes – who 'walks the walk while we talk the talk',
to her resilience against the odds as a Great War orphan,
her warmth, deep insights, wit and outrageous sense of fun.


## 'Quality of Life'

Someone who listens,
Someone to talk with
Kindness and understanding,
Someone to laugh with
'Me' to see 'me' a lot.
I like to be liked
I like to please
I like to know what pleases you
So that I can pass it on to someone else,
Doing things, loving people
Letting them know you are thinking of them,
I like to see the light come into their face because I have
    said something that really makes them happy,
…because I had so much unhappiness as a child
It is not so much about what people do but about relationships

**Edith Brooking, aged 97 (Rosemary's mother)**

## Appendix 1
# Resources for further reading

Please note that organisations are always updating the information they provide. All resources for further reading are correct at the time of printing but are subject to change. Please contact the organisation for the most up to date information.

### Age Concern England
Phone their information line 0800 00 99 66 or visit www.ageconcern.org.uk

### Factsheets
*Buying retirement housing* (17 pages)
*Finding help at home* (20 pages)
*Raising income or capital from your home* (18 pages)
*Direct payments from social services* (20 pages)
*Local authority assessment for community care services* (28 pages)
*Paying for care and support at home* (18 pages)
*Housing options* (22 pages)
*Older home owners – financial help with repairs and adaptations* (17 pages)
*NHS continuing healthcare, NHS-funded nursing care and intermediate care* (37 pages)
*Finding care home accommodation* (30 pages)
*Local authority charging procedures for care homes* (39 pages)

### Information guides
*How to find a care home* (20 pages)
*Help with care in your own home* (20 pages)
*Adapting your home* (24 pages)
*Living well in your home* (20 pages)
*What to do when someone dies* (20 pages)

### Alzheimer's Society
Phone their helpline 0845 300 0336 or visit www.alzheimers.org.uk

### Factsheets
*Adaptations, improvements and repairs to the home* (8 pages)
*Community care assessment* (8 pages)
*Direct payments* (4 pages)

*Enduring power of attorney, lasting power of attorney and receivership* (9 pages)
*Respite care* (6 pages)
*When does the local authority pay for care?* (4 pages)
*Assessments for NHS-funded nursing care* (6 pages)
*Choices in care* (9 pages)
*Paying care home fees* (8 pages)
*Selecting a care home* (9 pages)
*What standards of care can people expect from a care home?* (4 pages)
*Dealing with guilt* (6 pages)

## Arthritis Care
Tel: 0808 800 4050 (helpline) or visit www.arthritiscare.org.uk

### Factsheets
*Resources to help you exercise* (4 pages)
*Resources to help you manage your pain* (5 pages)

### Booklet
*Independent living and arthritis* (35 pages)

## Carers UK
Tel: 0808 808 7777 (carersline) or visit www.carersuk.org

### Factsheets
*Taking a break* (8 pages)
*Carers' allowance and the carer premium/carer addition* (8 pages)

### Booklets
*Looking after someone – a guide to carers' rights and benefits* (2007/8) (24 pages)
*Employees guide to working and caring* (28 pages)
*When caring comes to an end* (28 pages)

### Books
*Counsel and care, caring for loved ones in old age,* The Daily Telegraph and Lawpack (2007)
Bright L, Clark A *Moving Stories – the impact of admission into a care home on resident's partners*, The Relatives & Residents Association (2006)

### Counsel and Care

Tel: 0845 300 7585 (helpline) or visit www.counselandcare.org.uk

### Factsheets

*Help at home – what may be available in your local area* (32 pages)
*Home care – using direct payments* (41 pages)
*Housing decisions and options in later life* (33 pages)
*Care homes – what to look for* (21 pages)
*Care home fees – paying them in England* (44 pages),
*Scotland* (45 pages) and *Wales* (42 pages)
*Care home fees – third party top ups in England* (21 pages),
*Scotland* (22 pages) and *Wales* (20 pages)
*Continuing care – should the NHS be paying for your care?*
(28 pages)
*Practical information for coping with a death* (32 pages)

### Guides

*The Brief Care Home Guide* (2006) (26 pages)
*The Complete Care Home Guide* (2006) (72 pages)

### Disabled Living Foundation

Tel: 0845 130 9177 or visit www.dlf.org.uk

### Factsheets

*Choosing equipment to maintain safety and independence
at home (introducing telecare)* (18 pages)
*Choosing walking equipment* (25 pages)
*Choosing household equipment* (27 pages)
*Some suppliers of a range of daily living equipment* (5 pages)
*Clothing ideas for wheelchair users* (15 pages)
*Equipment to assist with dressing and putting on footwear*
(10 pages)
*A guide to simple communication products for daily living*
(22 pages)
*Sources of funding for obtaining equipment for older and
disabled people* (16 pages)

**The Elderly Accommodation Counsel**

Tel: 020 7820 1343 or visit www.housingcare.org

### Factsheets (all single- or double-sided A4)

*Paying for care (in England, Scotland, Wales or Northern Ireland)*

*Questions to ask about a care home*

### Booklets

*Accommodation Options for Older People* (13 pages)

*For You and Yours: An Introduction to Housing Options, Including Help to 'Stay Put', Moving to Sheltered or 'Extra Care' Housing, and Moving to a Care Home* (16 pages)

**Help the Aged**

Phone their SeniorLine on 0808 800 6565 or visit www.helptheaged.org.uk

### Factsheets

*Care at home* (22 pages)

*Equipment for daily living* (14 pages)

*Paying for your care home* (29 pages)

*Housing matters – your housing choices, advice for older people* (28 pages)

*Help in your home – getting support and care at home, advice for older people* (28 pages)

*Care homes – finding and paying for a care home, advice for older people* (34 pages)

### LifeGuide

*Caring for a Parent in Later Life* (2008) (£8.99)

**Parkinson's Disease Society**

Tel: 0808 800 0303 or visit www.parkinsons.org.uk

### Information sheets

*Living alone with Parkinson's* (8 pages)

*Falls and Parkinson's* (5 pages)

*Equipment and disability aids* (4 pages)

*Dementia and Parkinson's* (7 pages)

### Booklet

*Moving on… for people who have had Parkinson's for some time* (58 pages)

**Royal National Institute of Blind People**

Tel: 0845 766 9999 (helpline) or visit www.rnib.org.uk

**Factsheet**

*Lighting in your home*

**Royal National Institute for Deaf People**

Tel: 0808 808 0123 (helpline) or visit www.rnid.org.uk

**Factsheet**

*Free services – what benefits are available for deaf and hard of hearing people?* (9 pages)

**Booklets**

*Everyday solutions* (20 pages)

*Getting a hearing aid – how to use it and what to expect* (24 pages)

**Stroke Association**

Tel: 0845 303 3100 (helpline) or visit www.stroke.org.uk

*Stroke: a carer's guide* (7 pages)

*Accommodation after strokes* (4 pages)

**Best practice in care homes**

Several useful documents have been published recently looking at what are often called 'benchmarks', or standards we should expect in places where older people are receiving care.

The Social Institute for Excellence has a 'Dignity Challenge' listing ten aspects of dignity (www.scie.org.uk).

There are also activity provision benchmarks showing what you can expect to be provided (in terms of activities) in care homes. You can download these from the websites of the National Association of Providers of Activities (www.napa-activities.co.uk) and the College of Occupational Therapists (www.cot.org.uk).

The Relatives & Residents Association information series for relatives:

- *Clothing and laundry*
- *Continence care*
- *The contract*
- *Dying with dignity*
- *Feelings of guilt*
- *Food and mealtimes*
- *Privacy*
- *Relatives and decision making.*

These are available from www.relres.org

The Joseph Rowntree Foundation offers some useful good practice suggestions about night care: *Supporting older people in care homes at night* is available from www.jrf.org.uk

Finally, My Home Life has a series of short guides to aspects of good practice in care homes (available from www.myhomelife.org.uk). These include care home staff bulletins and research briefings:

- Issue 1 Care Home Staff Bulletin: *Managing transitions* (6 pages)
- Issue 2 Care Home Staff Bulletin: *Maintaining identity* (6 pages)
- Issue 3 Care Home Staff Bulletin: *Creating communities* (6 pages)
- Research Briefing No. 1: *Managing the transition to a care home* (4 pages)
- Research Briefing No. 2: *Maintaining identity* (5 pages)
- Research Briefing No. 3: *Creating community within care homes* (5 pages)
- Research Briefing No. 4: *Shared decision-making* (4 pages)
- Research Briefing No. 5: *Improving health and healthcare* (5 pages)
- Research Briefing No. 6: *Supporting good end of life* (4 pages)

## Appendix 2
# Contact details

### Age Concern

Age Concern provides a network of groups and a range of services for older people. These include information, advice and advocacy. Check your telephone directory for your local group. Age Concern Factsheets are a comprehensive guide to the issues that affect older people.

Astral House
1268 London Road
London SW16 4ER
Tel: 0800 00 99 66
www.ageconcern.org.uk

Age Concern will send you up to five fact sheets free of charge. Subjects include community care, consumer issues, health, income and benefits and leisure and learning. You can also subscribe to the factsheets or the free book catalogue on 020 8765 7200.

### Alzheimer's Society

Alzheimer's Society and Alzheimer Scotland offer specialist advice for people with dementia, their carers and their families. They produce a range of literature and publications providing local contacts and care home information. Local branches may run day care facilities and support groups.

Devon House
58 St Katharine's Way
London E1W 1JX
Tel: (8.30am–6.30pm, Monday to Friday) 0845 300 0336
www.alzheimers.org.uk  www.alzscot.org.uk

### Care Aware (Advocacy Service)

Their website offers independent information crucial to making informed decisions about long term care as a 'one stop' advice service (such as guidance or information on understanding social services assessment procedures, sourcing appropriate care home services and support, selecting an appropriate care home, establishing entitlement to state benefits, paying fees, accessing specialist support, protecting wishes and independence where there is a Power of Attorney).

Tel: 0870 513 4925
www.careaware.co.uk

## Care Directions

This is an information resource for middle aged 'children' needing to come to terms with a parent's care requirements and for older people themselves who want to know more about care options (such as choosing a care home, care agency, funding your choice and financial planning, sheltered housing, hospital discharge procedures and other care and legal matters) (www.caredirections.co.uk).

## Care Fees Investment Ltd

A partnership between Solicitors for the Elderly (SFE), Age Concern and the Elderly Accommodation Council has formed a company that specialises in long term care planning known as Care Fees Investment Ltd. They will help you with any difficulty relating to care fees planning and provide a jargon free report outlining the funding options to help you preserve your inheritance capital and any information on local authority entitlements and benefits. The initial consultation is free.

Tel: 0845 077 5655
www.carefeesinvestment.co.uk

## CareHome.co.uk

Care home search website for residential care homes and nursing homes in the UK. Produce an A–Z directory of care homes incorporating advice on care home fees (www.carehome.co.uk).

## The Care Select Helpline Service

This is a free information service, matching an individual's care requirements to suitable homes through a comprehensive database of UK registered providers of care.

Tel: 0800 389 2077 or use the on-line Care Select Helpline Service Form at www.carechoices.co.uk

## Cinnamon Trust

This is a specialist charity for older people and their pets. They help to find another home for your pet if you are unable to take it with you into a care home, provided prior arrangement has been made using a pet-friendly care home register. Pets must be registered before anyone needs a care home.

This can be done at any age with no charge. Once a pet is registered, the trust will continue help (such as walking the dog from the care home) as a seamless service.

10 Market Square
Hayle
Cornwall TR27 4HE
Tel: 01736 757900
www.cinnamon.org.uk

### Citizens Advice Bureau (CAB)

Provides free independent and confidential advice (face to face or by telephone) in your area (see phone directory for your local CAB).

### Counsel and Care

Twyman House
16 Bonny Street
London NW1 9PG
Tel: 0845 300 7585 (advice line)
www.counselandcare.org.uk

### Disabilities Care Register

This is a free public service. It allows anyone looking for care on behalf of an adult with disabilities to access information about appropriate care homes and services within a geographical area. They will send out information about homes direct and can arrange with you for the home to send you their brochures.

Tel: 0800 389 2077 or complete an on-line Disabilities Care Register form at www.carechoices.co.uk.

### The Disabled Living Foundation

This national charity provides free, impartial advice about all types of disability equipment and mobility products for older and disabled people, their carers and families. From stair-lifts to walk-in baths. You can speak to someone on the helpline or try out equipment in a demonstration centre, search their directory or find a factsheet. Topics include mobility, moving about the home, specialist clothing and footwear, communication equipment such as aids and alarms plus general information.

Tel: 0845 130 9177
www.dlf.org.uk

## Eldercare Solutions

Advice and information on how to go about finding a care home and what to look for. Eldercare provides a team of experts known as Care Companions. They offer guidance and advice on paying for care, different funding solutions, what to do with property, legal matters including wills and Powers of Attorney, inheritance tax and investment advice.

Suite 5
Wentworth Lodge
Great North Road
Welwyn Garden City
Hertfordshire AL8 7SR
Tel: 01707 368945

## Elderly Accommodation Counsel

Provides free advice to older people about their housing options. It has a comprehensive database on care homes in the UK focusing on aspects directly related to quality of life within a care home setting. The interactive website helps you through a range of options (http://hoop.eac.org.uk). The choices come under headings such as cost, comfort and design, quality of life, safety and security, independence, location, condition of property and managing at home. The website invites you to choose from a range of options what your problem areas are in these categories. For example, under the managing section, it might suggest problems such as using a bath, managing the garden or receiving visitors and it will provide possible solutions to each difficulty.

3rd Floor
89 Albert Embankment
London SE1 7TP
Tel: 020 7820 1343
www.housingcare.org

## English Community Care Association

The leading representative charity and membership organisation for independent care home providers that aims to promote high standards of health and social care in care homes (www.ecca.org.uk).

### Help the Aged

Provides free, impartial financial advice to help people plan their finances so that they can meet any future care costs and information on staying healthy and choosing a care home.

Tel: 0808 800 6565 (senior line)
www.helptheaged.org.uk

### My Home Life

This highly recommended resource provides care homes with information to help them to deliver quality care, share information, network with other care homes, provide information and help to share best practice information. Helpful poster briefings and fact sheets on a range of topics including relatives involvement, helping someone to settle into a care home (transitions) and keeping community links are written primarily for care staff, but may be also of interest to relatives and residents.

Their aim is to improve quality of life for residents of care homes, celebrate good practice and promote care homes as a positive option for those who need them (www.myhomelife.org.uk).

### National Association of Providers of Activities for Older People (NAPA)

NAPA is a registered charity and membership organisation for all those interested in increasing activity opportunities for older people in care settings. It provides an information line, publications and training in activity provision for care homes.

Bondway Commercial Centre
5th Floor
Unit 5.12
71 Bondway
London SW8 1SQ
Tel: 020 7078 9375
www.napa-activities.co.uk

### National Care Association

Established in 1981 to lobby government to benefit its members and those living in care homes and to represent them nationally.

Tel: 020 7831 7090
www.nca.gb.com

### National Care Forum

A representative body of the not for profit and social care providers with the main aim of providing quality outcomes for those using the services who are at the heart of quality. A list of not-for-profit homes available on www.nationalcareforum.co.uk NCF home search in the UK.

### Nursing Home Fees Agency (NHFA)

The NHFA's national team of care advisers combine their knowledge of financial advice with the complexities of the benefits system. They can guide you through the complexities of paying for care, match the best product to your situation and help you to know what you are entitled to. They can help you decide the most appropriate way to pay for care and understand what you are entitled to from the state. You can speak to a care fees adviser.

Tel: 0800 99 88 33 (local advisers available)
www.careuk.net

### Office of the Public Guardian

This office supports and promotes decision making for those who lack capacity or would like to plan for their future, within the framework of the Mental Capacity Act 2005. It provides information on how to choose someone to make decisions about finance, property ore health and welfare. It also provides information about what to do if you suspect someone is having difficulties or suffering abuse, making decisions on someone else's behalf or those wishing to apply to the Court of Protection.

Tel: 0845 330 2900
www.publicguardian.gov.uk

### Parliamentary and Health Service Ombudsman

This organisation offers little to the self funded resident but it works with local government as a free impartial and independent service. It considers complaints about the services provided through the NHS in England (such as continuing care funding, as a last resort service) after the complaints system has been exhausted through the local Primary Care Trust and Strategic Health Authority or Health Care Commission.

Tel: 0845 015 4033
www.ombudsman.org.uk

### Local Government Ombudsman
Tel: 0845 602 1983
www.lgo.org.uk

### Registered Nursing Home Association (RNHA)

Offers a directory of 1,300 member care homes in the UK.

Tel: 0800 074 0194
www.rnha.co.uk

### Relatives & Residents Association

This charity supports care home residents and their relatives and operates an advice line and other information services. It helps people and their relatives to make informed choices about moving into care. It also helps potential residents and their families make better informed decisions about what they have a right to and what standards they should expect. It represents the rights of the residents and campaigns for good practice.

24 The Ivories
6–18 Northampton Street
London N1 2HY
Tel: 020 7359 8136 (advice line)  Tel: 020 7359 8148 (office)
www.relres.org

### Solicitors for the Elderly

This national association of lawyers is concerned with improving the availability and delivery of specialist legal advice on legal issues that affect older and vulnerable people, their families and their carers.

Suite 17
Conbar House
Mead Lane
Hertford
Hertfordshire SG13 7AP
Tel: 0870 06 70 282
www.solicitorsfortheelderly.com

### Whereforcare

This website lists more than 20,000 care homes in UK and Northern Ireland, covering different types of specialist homes (for example, for people with multiple sclerosis or acquired brain injury). It contains care home reviews (www.whereforcare.co.uk).

### Other specialist organisations supporting different conditions include:

- The Parkinson's Disease Society
- British Heart Foundation
- Arthritis Care
- The Stroke Association

## Appendix 3
# A 'Walkabout Guide' for relatives of people with dementia

If you are looking for a care home providing care for people with dementia here are a few things you might like to look out for. They indicate there is a dementia sensitive environment which you can observe when you are looking for the right home. Good homes specialising in dementia will have paid attention to how they manage the environment from the perspective of the residents living there.

### Specialist environments for people with dementia

The social environment should recognise that 'all human life is grounded in relationships and that people with cognitive needs require an enriched social environment which both compensates for their impairment and fosters opportunities for personal growth' (University of Bradford 2006).

These ideas will give you some insight into the things that matter for people with dementia:

### What you can look for

● Are rooms left unattended by staff for long periods? Do residents appear content or are they bored and sleeping for long periods? Are people having a conversation ('passing pleasantries') or engaged in an activity?

● Is there is a 'homely' feel? With familiar objects/artefacts/ furniture and furnishings and pictures? Are areas decorated to feel different from each other using lighting and furnishing details with a domestic/family feel?

● Are staff helpful and kind? Do they engage in friendly conversation, showing attentiveness towards residents? Are residents addressed respectfully?

● Can communal areas be used for a variety of purposes? Can normal everyday activities and hobbies be seen taking place? Is there the opportunity to participate in a wide variety of activities throughout the week involving a range of people?

● Is there is an activity culture? Do staff encourage residents to join in simple activities (including domestic and familiar roles/activities around the home) as well as organised activity? Is attention paid to the little things that make a difference (such as how food and beverages are served)?

- Are there interesting items to stimulate all the senses and to help residents orientate (such as a fish tank, rummage baskets, reminiscence objects such as old kitchen objects, large picture books) readily accessible for residents and staff to use?
- Are long corridors broken up, where possible, with seating or landmarks – clocks, plants, windows, pictures, maps are examples of signs or cues to help orientate residents.
- Is there a range of books, music, DVDs and videos available for a range of tastes?
- Is radio and television use appropriate to the wishes and interests of residents? Are programmes and channels checked on a regular basis to ensure residents are offered a preference?
- Is it child-friendly? A box of books, toys, games and puzzles demonstrates that a home encourages children to visit.
- Is there is a secure and safe garden with comfortable seating, freely accessible to residents? Are there appropriate ramp rails with way-finding signs providing easy access to fresh air? Indoors, are there plants which provide a link with the natural world?
- Are there sensory features to stimulate interest indoors and outside (such as water features, wind chimes and colourful plantings).

Adapted with kind permission from J Pitkin (RCC Ltd)

# Appendix 4
# Activities

Having access to and being helped to get involved in meaningful activities is one of the most important areas for relatives.
It indicates care about the quality of life for their loved one. The list below provides some examples of different activities a home might provide and those suited to different stages of dementia.

**Activities for people at different stages of dementia**

| Stage of dementia | Potential activities |
|---|---|
| **Early dementia** | games, physical competitive games/sports, quizzes, discussions, end-product tasks, structured crafts for work-type activity |
| **Early to middle dementia** | music, dance, drama, art, poetry, reminiscence, story telling, festive/seasonal and spiritual activities |
| **Middle to late dementia** | movement, massage, cooking, stacking, rummaging, dolls and soft toys, balls, exercise, bubbles, balloons, gardening, folding, polishing, wiping, sweeping and 'clowning' to raise well-being |
| **Late dementia** | singing, rocking, holding, non-verbal communication, smiling, stroking, reflex responses to direct stimulation. |

Different types of activity may vary according to the changing needs and preferences of residents and encourage:

- creativity
- cultural interest
- esteem needs
- emotional expression and mood
- intellectual/cognitive stimulation
- physical activity
- relaxation and recreation
- sensory experience
- social interaction and community/family
- spiritual expression.

Activities should also focus on the quality of relationships and foster a sense of security, continuity, belonging, purpose, fulfilment and a sense of significance. They should also include well-being, communicating and making choices, making contact with other people, showing warmth, enjoyment, alertness and responsiveness, using remaining abilities, creative expression, helpfulness, responding appropriately, expressing emotions appropriately, relaxed posture/body language, sense of humour, purpose and signs of self-respect (Bradford Dementia Group, Well-being profiling).

The ideas below are broad and will not suit everyone as it is important to match the activity to the interests and abilities of the individuals. If you want to get involved, liaise with the activity co-ordinator. They will know more about who would enjoy participating. Many homes will welcome assistance and involvement from relatives in the community life of the home. Check with your activity co-ordinator or manager how you can offer your services to the activities within the home.

### General activity ideas

| | |
|---|---|
| **Stimulating the mind (different challenges for different abilities)** | word games (anagrams, crosswords, hangman, word target, word chains), quizzes (general knowledge/current affairs related to both national and local area), commercially available kits and games (dominos, picture matching), debates, newspaper discussions, memory games (such as Kim's Game), talking through an activity sequence (such as putting on a tie or tea-making), completing proverbs, 3–12+ piece puzzles made from a favourite picture/subject, bridge or bingo (depending on what is ability and interest) |
| **Encouraging communication** | discussions; drama (mime, story-making, reminiscence; reading and writing), social activities, being involved in all care activities |
| **Expressing creativity** | art (marbling, printing, silk and glass painting), crafts (candle making, needlecrafts, pottery, salt-dough modelling, wax rubbing, weaving and simple woodwork), creative writing, poetry, stories, life histories and computer-based activities |
| **Enjoying music** | reminiscence, theme-based quizzes, games/painting to music, music appreciation, music making/playing music and singing |

| Encouraging movement and exercise | ball games, balloons, batons and scarves, carpet bowls, darts, hockey, hoop-la, parachute, skittles, seated exercises. Encourage mobility throughout home environment, singing songs and hymns together |
|---|---|
| Fun, relaxation, recreation and every day activity | cookery, gardening, pets, reading, woodwork, singing. Dressing up (hats, gloves, colourful scarves). Looking at large picture books/colourful picture magazines. Bring in some soft toys/dolls, interesting objects to pass round, to jog memories or conversation. Listen to old favourites. Visit with children/pets. Polishing, washing, tidying and sorting: pub-type games |
| Enjoying culture | variety of discussions with examples – poetry, theatre, music, art. Slide shows, talks about travel, hobbies and topics of interest |
| Remembering how things used to be | discussions using props, outings, links with local libraries and schools, intergenerational projects with young people, singing |
| Working with the 5 senses | 'smelly' and 'feely' quizzes, pets being brought in, cooking, herbs, flowers, pictures, objects, smelling games, listening to sounds/music, passing round interesting textured fabrics, furs or clothes stimulating touch, taste, smell and sight |
| Enjoying social interaction | group activities, games, quizzes, outings, tea dances and parties, group singing. Bring in some special cakes/food. Have tea out of china cups. Have a sherry with all the 'extras' |
| Meeting spiritual and religious needs | music, singing spiritual songs, photography – particularly plants and nature, hymn singing – short meditations or readings and short services. |

Adapted from Hurtley R, Wenborn J (2004)

# Appendix 5
# Communicating with your relative

Good communication is the foundation of any relationship and the basis of a good caring community. These simple tips might help you to maintain contact with the person you are visiting. It can be challenging if you have not been given any advice from elsewhere.

### Involving a relative who has sensory or communication difficulties

Listed below are some suggestions for those who may find it difficult to talk to their family members due to practical difficulties arising from impairment. The following guidelines may be helpful to help them as much as possible:

- talk slightly slower than usual using clear and simple sentences
- give one piece of information at a time
- use familiar words and phrases which are more easily understood but avoid patronising
- abilities can fluctuate (particularly if a person has dementia) so do not underestimate their ability or capacity to make decisions
- allow enough time for the person to take in the information and respond to questions
- be prepared to repeat questions
- avoid completing people's sentences for them.

### Effective communication with people who have impaired hearing

There are six basic rules:

1 let your face be seen
2 do not cover your mouth
3 speak slowly and clearly
4 rephrase or write things down
5 be patient
6 avoid background noise.

Simple techniques are often overlooked.

## Tips to help lip readers

As the speaker:

- face the lip reader
- have the source of light on your face
- ensure sufficient lip movement without distorting your face
- speak slightly more slowly
- stand about one metre away
- give contextual clues at the beginning of a conversation
- talk in phrases and short sentences, not single words
- gain the lip reader's attention before saying anything
- check that any instructions are being fully understood
- avoid sudden changes of topic
- inform the lip reader when you are going to change the topic being discussed
- keep your head still and your mouth visible
- use visual cues and write things down if necessary.

## Don't:

- move about
- walk away while speaking
- stand with your back to the light
- exaggerate your lip shapes
- speak very slowly, nor very quickly
- use distracting hand movements.

## Remember:

- heavy beards and moustaches may make lip reading difficult
- lively facial expressions and gestures are helpful
- although lip reading is a support, it can be unreliable. Many words look the same on the lips (such as 'pen', 'men' and 'Ben'; 'choose' and 'shoes')
- if the lip reader does not understand, do not just repeat (or shout) the same words. Re-phrase them
- lip reading is a strain and may cause fatigue over long periods.

## Effective communication with people who have impaired vision

- gain the listener's attention
- face the person directly at eye level
- do not touch the person until they are aware of your presence
- use large gestures and non-verbal demonstration as necessary
- reassure the person and reinforce your instructions with visual, auditory and tactile (touch) cues
- distribute lighting evenly around the room
- provide enough light from behind
- eliminate sources of glare, bright light and reflection
- allow the person time to accommodate changes in distance and lighting
- use large-print books, signs and instructions with clear contrast and definition
- if words or numbers are being written on cards for an activity, use black on a yellow background rather than on a white background
- watch out for signs of misunderstanding
- identify the topic of conversation to provide additional cues to the listener.

## Effective communication with people who have speech and language difficulties

- reduce background noise (for example, use a tablecloth to reduce the noise of china, turn off the television/radio)
- face the person at eye level
- speak clearly and deliberately
- slow down your speech
- use vocal inflections to express feelings and emphasis
- use gestures and facial expressions
- use the person's name at beginning of the sentence
- keep sentences short
- keep content clear and concise
- avoid open questions. Ask questions that require 'yes' or 'no' in reply or a gesture
- say the same thing in different ways
- do not change the subject too quickly
- reduce potential confusion. Be specific about times and places, and use prompts

- use 'concrete' language. Jokes, facetiousness and implied meanings can be misinterpreted
- repeat important information at intervals if the person's short term memory is affected
- enhance communication by showing warmth, appreciation and approval
- always explain what you are doing and why
- allow the person plenty of time to respond
- do not interrupt or speak on behalf of the other person
- do not pretend that you understand if you don't. Do demonstrate that you are attending to what they are saying
- encourage the person to use gestures.

### Effective communication with people who have dementia

Remember that people experience mood swings which might be influenced by both the physical, social and environmental factors:

- **physical** – pain, discomfort, need for the lavatory, energy levels
- **emotional** – the quality of relationship, presence of others, whether or not spiritual needs are being met
- **environmental** – pacing, timing, concentration, attention, time of day or night, affect of preceding event or intervention, staff attitude/relationships and organisational factors.

Adapted from Allen 2001

### When visiting a relative who has dementia think about your:

- **Tone of voice** – project warmth, approachability, firmness, confidence rather than anger or threat

- **Gesture and posture** – body posture should convey interest, equal eye contact level, with affirming nods, smiles and hand gestures

- **Listening and hearing** – pick out the underlying theme and the emotional tone behind from repetitive dysphasic speech from repeated words, phrases or accompanying behaviour. Use concrete words and familiar topics

- **Reflection** – reflecting back words can be helpful to aid understanding meanings. Focus on the emotional content of what is being said, regardless of its relevance to the here-and-now situation (validation)

- **Touch** – this can provide a sense of reassurance and comfort when eyesight or hearing is diminished. Different cultures have different norms but it is usually safe to use the hand, arm or shoulder area for touch
- **Observation** – observations of non-verbal behaviour such as body language, facial expressions, movement, breathing, posture can say a lot about the state of well-being.

Adapted from *The Successful Activity Co-ordinator* (2005) Hurtley R, Wenborn J

**Additional tips:**

- consider what might be the optimum time of day, and avoid times of fatigue and drowsiness such as after lunch or a tiring activity
- check that glasses, hearing aids and dentures are worn, and that they fit correctly
- minimise distractions
- identify yourself on every visit
- address the person by their preferred name
- maximise the use of eye contact at eye level
- encourage a person to concentrate. Do not rush them
- speak calmly, clearly and slowly. Give one chunk of information at a time, ensuring the person has understood it
- use simple, short sentences
- use orientation tools, time and place, day, weather, season, for mildly impaired residents using cues, reminders and prompts
- use pictures rather than words
- use rhyme, repetition and rhythm
- use humour
- use colour rather than black and white images
- use objects, symbols and gestures as well as spoken communication
- introduce one question at a time
- maximise non-verbal responses with smiles and head nods, holding hands
- use key words, and reduce the number of unimportant words
- use gesture and pointing
- make associations using songs, rhymes, word association or picture association
- give the person enough time to respond

- keep sessions short and interesting, rather than too long
- respond to the emotion behind the words. Feelings can be real even if the words are inappropriate
- provide a reason for communication. Use interesting objects and pictures to talk about. Use reminiscence as a communication tool in formal and informal situations
- praise responses to increase confidence
- use memory games such as 'Kim's Game', pairs or reminiscing
- if a person forgets what they have just said, recap by repeating it back (if relevant) or gently remind them of the subject being discussed
- exaggerate and emphasise key points
- use the senses to trigger memory.

## Appendix 6
## Considerations when taking a pet into a care home

Some care homes try to accommodate a pet as the health benefits of human and animal companionship are acknowledged. But it depends on the culture and type of home whether pets are welcome. Consider the individual home's policy. Where it is possible to take a pet in find out:

- who will be responsible for ensuring the pet is let outside?
- how safe are the grounds?
- who pays for the food?
- who takes responsibility for exercising, feeding and walking the dog?
- who cleans out the bird cage?
- do you need to do this yourself or arrange it with a volunteer or staff?
- are there any additional costs?
- what happens if the dog is ill or the resident is admitted to hospital?
- who takes responsibility for the welfare of the pet?
- what happens if the pet does not settle into the home?
- what happens if other residents don't like the animal?

# Index

## About Age Concern

Age Concern is the UK's largest organisation working for and with older people to enable them to make more of life. A federation of over 400 independent charities that share the same name, values and standards, we believe that later life should be fulfilling, enjoyable and productive.

Age Concern publishes a wide range of bestselling books that help thousands of people each year. Our books provide practical, trusted advice on a range of subjects, from finance and retirement planning to health and surfing the web. Whether you are acting as a carer or want to know more about your rights to healthcare or employment, we have something for everyone.

**To find out more, to order a free catalogue or to buy a book please call our hotline on 0870 44 22 120 or visit the website at www.ageconcern.org.uk/bookshop. You can also buy our books from all good bookshops.**

### Age Concern England

1268 London Road
London SW16 4ER

Tel: 020 8765 7200
www.ageconcern.org.uk

### Age Concern Cymru

Ty John Pathy
Units 13 and 14 Neptune Court
Vanguard Way
Cardiff CF24 5PJ

Tel: 029 2043 1555
www.accymru.org.uk

### Age Concern Scotland

Causewayside House
160 Causewayside
Edinburgh EH9 1PR

Tel: 0845 833 0200
www.ageconcernscotland.org.uk

### Age Concern Northern Ireland

3 Lower Crescent
Belfast BT7 1NR

Tel: 028 9024 5729
www.ageconcernni.org

Age Concern Information: we produce a range of comprehensive information guides designed to answer many of the questions that older people – or those advising them – may have. These free guides cover issues such as housing, care homes, pensions, benefits, health, community care, leisure and education, and can be obtained by calling our free information line on 0800 00 99 66 or by downloading them from the website (www.ageconcern.org.uk).